Selected Solutions Manual

Matthew E. Johll
St. Norbert College

Introductory Chemistry

Nivaldo J. Tro

Prentice
Hall

Upper Saddle River, NJ 07458

Project Manager: Kristen Kaiser
Senior Editor: Kent Porter-Hamann
Editor-in-Chief: John Challice
Executive Managing Editor: Kathleen Schiaparelli
Assistant Managing Editor: Dinah Thong
Production Editor: Elizabeth Klug
Supplement Cover Manager: Paul Gourhan
Supplement Cover Designer: Joanne Alexandris
Manufacturing Buyer: Ilene Kahn
Cover Illustrator: Quade Paul

© 2003 by Pearson Education, Inc.
Pearson Education, Inc.
Upper Saddle River, NJ 07458

Printed in the United States of America

10 9 8 7 6 5

ISBN 0-13-100201-5

Pearson Education Ltd., *London*
Pearson Education Australia Pty. Ltd., *Sydney*
Pearson Education Singapore, Pte. Ltd.
Pearson Education North Asia Ltd., *Hong Kong*
Pearson Education Canada, Inc., *Toronto*
Pearson Educación de Mexico, S.A. de C.V.
Pearson Education—Japan, *Tokyo*
Pearson Education Malaysia, Pte. Ltd.
Pearson Education, *Upper Saddle River, New Jersey*

Table of Contents

The Chemical World

Problems

1. Soda contains carbon dioxide molecules that are forced into a mixture with water molecules because of the increased pressure. Opening the can of soda will release the pressure, which allows the carbon dioxide to escape from the mixture and form bubbles.

3. Chemists study the world around us and try to explain how it works. By studying the interactions of atoms and molecules, chemists hope to better understand the world around us.

5. Chemistry: The science that seeks to understand what matter does by studying what atoms and molecules do.

7. The scientific method is a way of approaching a problem that emphasizes making observations, planning experiments, and then using logic to come to a conclusion.

9. A scientific law is a brief statement that summarizes previous observations and can be used to predict the results of future related experiments. The scientific law does not explain why the observations occur, that is the role of a scientific theory.

11. A scientific theory is the best current explanation of a phenomenon that has been validated by years worth of experiments.

13. John Dalton proposed his atomic theory, which states that all matter is composed of small, indestructible particles called atoms.

Problems

15. a) observation
    b) theory
    c) law
    d) observation

17. a) The reactivity of a chemical is proportional to the molecular size.
    b) Reactivity is due to the momentum of collisions, and because the larger molecules have a greater momentum, they have a greater reactivity.
    Remember this problem is for an imaginary universe!

Measurement and Problem Solving

Questions

1. Units must be included with a number so that there is no doubt as to the meaning of the number. For example, if you reported a weight of 5, that would be unclear. However if you reported a weight of 5 grams, there would be no confusion.

3. Scientific notation is used to make very small numbers and very large numbers easier to write and to understand.

5. a) Zeros in the middle of two other numbers ARE significant.
   b) Zeros at the end of a number with a decimal point ARE significant.
   c) Zeros at the beginning of a number are NOT significant.
   d) Zeros at the end of a number with no decimal point are ambiguous. Avoid using these numbers and use scientific notation instead.

7. The number of significant digits in multiplication and division problems is determined by whichever number contains the fewest significant digits.

9. Only consider the first digit that is going to be dropped, numbers beyond that are irrelevant. If that number is four or less, round down. If the number is five or higher, round up.

11. The SI unit for length is the meter (m), for mass is the kilogram (kg), and for time is the second (s).

13. The frisbee would be measured in meters with a prefix of deci (0.1). One might choose to use prefix of centi (0.01), as it tends to be more commonly used.

15. Correct answers may vary based on the accuracy of the ruler.

17. Units are very important in calculations because they give us information on how we should go about converting one unit to another, and they help prevent confusion.

19. A conversion factor is a fraction of two equivalent quantities is used to convert information from one set of units to another.

21. grams → pounds

$$\frac{1 \text{ lb}}{453.6 \text{ g}}$$

23. meters → centimeters → inches → feet

$$\frac{100 \text{ cm}}{1 \text{ m}} \qquad \frac{1 \text{ in}}{2.54 \text{ cm}} \qquad \frac{1 \text{ ft}}{12 \text{ in}}$$

25. Density is the ratio of the mass of an object to the volume of the object. Objects that have a large density are perceived to be heavy. Objects that have a small density are perceived to be light. Density can work as a conversion factor because it is an equality that converts between mass and volume. For example, 1 gram of water will occupy a volume of 1 mL. Therefore if you have a mass of 100 grams you can use the density to calculate the volume.

Problems

Scientific Notation

27. a) 3.2667×10^7
    b) 1.193×10^6
    c) 1.8175×10^7
    d) 4.81×10^5

29. a) 7.461×10^{-11} m
    b) 1.57×10^{-5} mi
    c) 6.32×10^{-7} m
    d) 1.5×10^{-5} m

31. <u>Decimal Notation</u>   <u>Scientific Notation</u>
    0.000874 $\underline{8.74 \times 10^{-4}}$

    <u>34560000000</u> 3.456×10^{10}

    100,000,000 $\underline{1 \times 10^8}$

    <u>9800000000000</u> 9.8×10^{12}

33. a) 602,200,000,000,000,000,000,000 atoms
    b) 0.00000000000000000016 C
    c) 299,000,000 m/s
    d) 344 m/s

35. a) 3,890,000,000
    b) 0.00059
    c) 8,680,000,000,000
    d) 0.0000000786

Significant Figures

37. a) 54.9 mL
    b) 48.7 °C
    c) 5.53 mL
    d) 46.83 °C

39. a) 0.00<u>6</u>08

    b) 45<u>0</u>,8<u>02</u>

    c) 0.000000000000000005

    d) 0.00<u>9090</u>

41. a) 4
    b) 4
    c) ambiguous: 4 possibly 5
    d) 6

43. | Number | Significant Figures | |
    |--------|---------------------|--|
    | a) 895675 | 6 | *correct* |
    | b) 0.000869 | 6 | *incorrect, 3: leading zeros are not significant* |
    | c) 0.5672100 | 5 | *incorrect, 7: terminal zeros are significant* |
    | d) 6.022×10^{23} | 4 | *correct* |

Rounding

45. a) 343.0
    b) 0.009651
    c) 3.526×10^{-8}
    d) 1.127×10^9

47. a) 2.3
    b) 2.4
    c) 2.3
    d) 2.4

49. a) incorrect, 42.3
    b) correct
    c) correct
    d) incorrect, 0.0456

Significant Figures in Calculations

51. a) 0.054
    b) 0.619
    c) 1.2×10^8
    d) 6.6

53. a) Incorrect, 4.22×10^3
    b) Correct
    c) Incorrect, 3.9969
    d) Correct

55. a) 200.6
    b) 41.4
    c) 183.3
    d) 1.22

57. a) correct
    b) incorrect, 1.0982
    c) correct
    d) incorrect, 3.53

59. a) 3.9×10^3
    b) 632
    c) 8.93×10^4
    d) 6.34

61. a) incorrect, 3.15×10^3
    b) correct
    c) correct
    d) correct

63. a) $2.14 \text{ kg} \times \dfrac{1000 \text{ g}}{1 \text{ kg}} = 2.14 x 10^{3} \text{ g}$

    b) $6172 \text{ mm} \times \dfrac{1 \text{ m}}{1000 \text{ mm}} = 6.172 \text{ m}$

    c) $1316 \text{ mg} \times \dfrac{1 \text{ g}}{1000 \text{ mg}} \times \dfrac{1 \text{ kg}}{1000 \text{ g}} = 1.316 x 10^{-3} \text{ kg}$

    d) $0.0256 \text{ L} \times \dfrac{1000 \text{ mL}}{1 \text{ L}} = 25.6 \text{ mL}$

65. a) $22.5 \text{ in} \times \dfrac{2.54 \text{ cm}}{1 \text{ in}} = 57.2 \text{ cm}$

    b) $126 \text{ ft} \times \dfrac{12 \text{ in}}{1 \text{ ft}} \times \dfrac{2.54 \text{ cm}}{1 \text{ in}} \times \dfrac{1 \text{ m}}{100 \text{ cm}} = 38.4 \text{ m}$

    c) $825 \text{ yd} \times \dfrac{1 \text{ m}}{1.094 \text{ yd}} \times \dfrac{1 \text{ km}}{1000 \text{ m}} = 0.754 \text{ km}$

    d) $2.4 \text{ in} \times \dfrac{2.54 \text{ cm}}{1 \text{ in}} \times \dfrac{10 \text{ mm}}{1 \text{ cm}} = 61 \text{ mm}$

67. a) $40 \text{ cm} \times \dfrac{1 \text{ in}}{2.54 \text{ cm}} = 16 \text{ in}$

    b) $27.8 \text{ m} \times \dfrac{39.37 \text{ in}}{1 \text{ m}} \times \dfrac{1 \text{ ft}}{12 \text{ in}} = 91.2 \text{ ft}$

    c) $10 \text{ km} \times \dfrac{0.6214 \text{ mi}}{1 \text{ km}} = 6.2 \text{ mi}$

    d) $3845 \text{ kg} \times \dfrac{2.205 \text{ lb}}{1 \text{ kg}} = 8478 \text{ lb}$

69. $2.4 \text{ lb} \times \dfrac{453.59 \text{ g}}{1 \text{ lb}} = 1.1 x 10^{3} \text{ g}$

71. $10.0 \text{ km} \times \dfrac{0.6214 \text{ mi}}{1 \text{ km}} \times \dfrac{1 \text{ hr}}{7.5 \text{ mi}} \times \dfrac{60 \text{ min}}{1 \text{ hr}} = 50 \text{ min}$

73. $5.0 \text{ qt} \times \dfrac{1 \text{ L}}{1.057 \text{ qt}} \times \dfrac{1000 \text{ cm}^3}{1 \text{ L}} = 4.7 \times 10^3 \text{cm}^3$

Units Raised to a Power

75. a) $1.0 \text{ km}^2 \times \dfrac{(1000 \text{ m})^2}{(1 \text{ km})^2} = 1.0 \times 10^6 \text{ m}^2$

   b) $1.0 \text{ cm}^3 \times \dfrac{(1 \text{ m})^3}{(100 \text{ cm})^3} = 1.0 \times 10^{-6} \text{ m}^3$

   c) $1.0 \text{ mm}^3 \times \dfrac{(1 \text{m})^3}{(1000 \text{ mm})^3} = 1.0 \times 10^{-9} \text{ m}^3$

77. a) $215 \text{ m}^2 \times \dfrac{(1 \text{ km})^2}{(1000 \text{ m})^2} = 2.15 \times 10^{-4} \text{ km}^2$

   b) $215 \text{ m}^2 \times \dfrac{(10 \text{ dm})^2}{(1 \text{ m})^2} = 2.15 \times 10^4 \text{ dm}^2$

   c) $215 \text{ m}^2 \times \dfrac{(100 \text{ cm})^2}{(1 \text{ m})^2} = 2.15 \times 10^6 \text{ cm}^2$

79. 954 million acres = 954,000,000 acres = 9.54×10^8 acres;

   $9.54 \times 10^8 \text{ acres} \times \dfrac{43,560 \text{ ft}^2}{1 \text{ acre}} \times \dfrac{(1 \text{ mi})^2}{(5280 \text{ ft})^2} = 1.49 \times 10^6 \text{ mi}^2$

Density

81. $d = \dfrac{35.4 \text{ g}}{3.11 \text{ cm}^3} = 11.4 \text{ g/cm}^3$ Which matches the density of lead.

83. $d = \dfrac{3.15 \times 10^3}{2.50 \text{ L}} \times \dfrac{1 \text{ L}}{1000 \text{ mL}} \times \dfrac{1 \text{ mL}}{1 \text{ cm}^3} = 1.26 \text{ g/cm}^3$

85. $d = \dfrac{206 \text{ grams}}{10.7 \text{ mL}} \times \dfrac{1 \text{ mL}}{1 \text{ cm}^3} = 19.3 \text{ g/cm}^3$;

Yes, the density matches gold.

87. a) $417 \text{ mL} \times \dfrac{1 \text{ cm}^3}{1 \text{ mL}} \times \dfrac{1.11 \text{ g}}{1 \text{ cm}^3} = 463 \text{ g}$

b) $4.1 \text{ kg} \times \dfrac{1000 \text{ g}}{1 \text{ kg}} \times \dfrac{1 \text{ cm}^3}{1.11 \text{ g}} \times \dfrac{1 \text{ L}}{1000 \text{ cm}^3} = 3.7 \text{ L}$

Cumulative Problems

89. a) $d = \dfrac{m}{V} \Rightarrow m = d \times V$

$$m_{gold} = 19.3 \dfrac{g}{cm^3} \times 1.75 \text{ L} \times \dfrac{1000 \text{ cm}^3}{1 \text{ L}} = 3.38 x 10^4 g$$

$$m_{sand} = 3.00 \dfrac{g}{cm^3} \times 1.75 \text{ L} \times \dfrac{1000 \text{ cm}^3}{1 \text{ L}} = 5.25 x 10^3 g$$

b) Yes, the thief set off the alarm because the sand was much lighter than the gold vase.

91. $d = \dfrac{8.56 \text{ lbs}}{22.4 \text{ in}^3} \times \dfrac{453.59 \text{ g}}{1 \text{ lb}} \times \dfrac{(1 \text{ in})^3}{(2.54 \text{ cm})^3} = 10.6 \text{ g/cm}^3$

93. $d = 2.7 \dfrac{g}{cm^3} \times \dfrac{1 \text{ lb}}{453.59 \text{ g}} \times \dfrac{(2.54 \text{ cm})^3}{(1 \text{ in})^3} = 0.098 \text{ lb/in}^3$

95. $150 \text{ yd}^3 \times \dfrac{(1 \text{ m})^3}{(1.094 \text{ yd})^3} \times \dfrac{(100 \text{ cm})^3}{(1 \text{ m})^3} \times \dfrac{1.0 \text{ g}}{1 \text{ cm}^3} \times \dfrac{1 \text{ lb}}{453.59 \text{ g}} = 2.5 x 10^5 \text{ lbs}$

97. $\dfrac{70 \text{ mi}}{1 \text{ gal}} \times \dfrac{1 \text{ gal}}{3.785 \text{ L}} \times \dfrac{1 \text{ km}}{0.6214 \text{ mi}} = 30 \text{ km/L}$

99. $1.55 \times 10^5 \, \text{ft} \times \dfrac{0.3048 \, \text{m}}{1 \, \text{ft}} \times \dfrac{1 \, \text{km}}{1000 \, \text{m}} = 47.2 \, \text{km}$

$155 \, \text{km} - 47.2 = 108 \, \text{km}$ difference in altitude.

The orbiter would have attempted to establish an orbit of 47.2 km above Mars.

101. $m = \left(1 \times 10^3\right)\left(2.0 \times 10^{30} \, \text{kg}\right)\dfrac{1000 \, \text{g}}{1 \, \text{kg}} = 2.0 \times 10^{36} \, \text{g}$

$V = 4/3 \;\; (3.14) \left(\dfrac{2.16 \times 10^3 \, \text{mi}}{2}\right)^3 = 5.27 \times 10^9 \, \text{mi}^3$

$V = 5.27 \times 10^9 \, \text{mi}^3 \times \dfrac{(1 \, \text{km})^3}{(0.6214 \, \text{mi})^3} \times \dfrac{(1000 \, \text{m})^3}{(1 \, \text{km})^3} \times \dfrac{(100 \, \text{cm})^3}{(1 \, \text{m})^3}$

$= 2.20 \times 10^{25} \, \text{cm}^3$

$d = \dfrac{2.0 \times 10^{36} \, \text{g}}{2.20 \times 10^{25} \, \text{cm}^3} = 9.1 \times 10^{10} \, \text{g/cm}^3$

Matter and Energy

Questions

1. Matter is defined as anything that occupies space and has mass. It can be thought of as the physical material that makes up the universe.

3. Matter can be found as either a solid, a liquid, or a gas.

5. A crystalline solid has atoms arranged in a repeating geometric pattern, whereas an amorphous solid has atoms that do not form repeating patterns.

7. A gas has no fixed volume or shape. Rather, it assumes both the shape and the volume of the container it occupies.

9. A mixture is composed of two or more pure substances that have been mixed together in a variable proportion.

11. A pure substance is composed of only one type of atom or one type of molecule.

13. A mixture is formed when two or more pure substances are mixed together, but a new substance is not formed. A compound is formed when two or more elements are bonded together to form a new substance.

15. A physical change is one that does not alter the chemical composition of a compound. A chemical change, however, will alter the chemical composition of a compound.

17. Energy is the capacity to do work.

19. Potential energy, kinetic energy, electrical energy, chemical energy, thermal energy

21. Temperature can be measured by the Fahrenheit scale (°F), the Celsius scale (°C), and the Kelvin scale (K).

23. Heat capacity is a measure of how much heat is needed to raise the temperature of a given substance by 1°C.

25. $°C = \dfrac{\left[°F - 32\right]}{1.8} \Rightarrow 1.8 \times °C = [°F - 32] \Rightarrow °F = (1.8 \times °C) + 32$

Problems

Classifying Matter

27. a) element
    b) element
    c) compound
    d) compound

29. a) homogeneous
    b) heterogeneous
    c) homogeneous
    d) homogeneous

31. a) pure, element
    b) mixture, homogeneous
    c) mixture, heterogeneous
    d) mixture, heterogeneous

Physical and Chemical Properties and Physical and Chemical Changes

33. a) chemical
    b) physical
    c) physical
    d) chemical

35. Physical Properties: colorless, odorless, gas at room temperature, one liter has a mass of 1.260 g under standard conditions, mixes with acetone.
    Chemical Properties: flammable, polymerizes to form polyethylene

37. a) chemical
    b) physical
    c) chemical
    d) chemical

39. a) physical
    b) chemical

The Conservation of Mass

41. Mass of reactants = Mass of products; 42 kg + 168 kg = 210 kg

43. a) Yes. 54 g reactants = 54 g products
    b) No. 276 g reactants ≠ 267 g products

11

45. Mass of reactants = Mass of products

9.7 g + 34.7g = 29.3g + g water ⟹

g water = 44.4 - 29.3 = 15.1 g

Conversion of Energy Units

47. a) $32.5 \text{ J} \times \dfrac{1 \text{ cal}}{4.184 \text{ J}} = 7.77 \text{ cal}$

b) $562 \text{ cal} \times \dfrac{4.184 \text{ J}}{1 \text{ cal}} = 2.35 \times 10^3 \text{ cal}$

c) $35.7 \text{ kJ} \times \dfrac{1000 \text{ J}}{1 \text{ kJ}} \times \dfrac{1 \text{ cal}}{4.184 \text{ J}} = 8.53 \times 10^3 \text{ cal}$

d) $287 \text{ cal} \times \dfrac{4.184 \text{ J}}{1 \text{ cal}} \times \dfrac{1 \text{ kJ}}{1000 \text{ J}} = 1.20 \text{ kJ}$

49. a) $25 \text{ kWh} \times \dfrac{3.60 \times 10^6 \text{ J}}{1 \text{ kWh}} = 9.0 \times 10^7 \text{ J}$

b) $249 \text{ cal} \times \dfrac{1 \text{ Cal}}{1000 \text{ cal}} = 0.249 \text{ Cal}$

c) $113 \text{ cal} \times \dfrac{4.184 \text{ J}}{1 \text{ cal}} \times \dfrac{1 \text{ kWh}}{3.60 \times 10^6 \text{ J}} = 1.31 \times 10^{-4} \text{ kWh}$

d) $44 \text{ kJ} \times \dfrac{1000 \text{ J}}{1 \text{ kJ}} \times \dfrac{1 \text{ cal}}{4.184 \text{ J}} = 1.1 \times 10^4 \text{ cal}$

51. $955 \text{ kWh} \times \dfrac{3.60 \times 10^6 \text{ J}}{1 \text{ kWh}} = 3.44 \times 10^9 \text{ J}$

53. $2.0 \times 10^3 \text{ Cal} \times \dfrac{1000 \text{ cal}}{1 \text{ Cal}} \times \dfrac{4.184 \text{ J}}{1 \text{ cal}} = 8.4 \times 10^6 \text{ J}$

55. a) $°C = \dfrac{\left[°F - 32\right]}{1.8} = \dfrac{\left[212 - 32\right]}{1.8} = \dfrac{180}{1.8} = 100\,°C$

b) $°C = K - 273 = 77 - 273 = -196\,°C$

$°F = (1.8 \times °C) + 32 = (1.8 \times -196) + 32 = -3.2 x10^2\,°F$

c) $K = 273 + °C = 273 + 25 = 298\ K$

d) $°C = \dfrac{\left[°F - 32\right]}{1.8} = \dfrac{\left[98.6 - 32\right]}{1.8} = 37\,°C; \quad K = 273 + °C = 310\ K$

57. $°C = \dfrac{\left[°F - 32\right]}{1.8} = \dfrac{\left[-80 - 32\right]}{1.8} = \dfrac{-112}{1.8} = -62\,°C$

$K = 273 + °C = 273 + -62 = 2.1 x10^2\ K$

59. $°F = (1.8 \times °C) + 32 = (1.8 \times -114) + 32 = -205.2 + 32 = -173\,°F$

$K = 273 + °C = 273 + -114 = 159\ K$

Energy, Heat Capacity, and Temperature Changes

61. $97\ g \times \dfrac{4.184\ J}{g\ °C} \times (67\,°C - 42\,°C) = 1.0 x10^4 J$

63. $45\ kg \times \dfrac{1000\ g}{1\ kg} \times \dfrac{2.42\ J}{g\ °C} \times (19°C - 11°C) = 8.7 x10^5 J$

65. $89\ J = 12\ g \times \dfrac{0.128\ J}{g\ °C} \times (\Delta T) \Rightarrow \Delta T = \dfrac{89\ J}{12\ g \times \dfrac{0.128\ J}{g\ °C}} = 58\,°C$

67. $15\ J = 12\ g \times \dfrac{0.449\ J}{g\ °C} \times (T_f - 28°C) \Rightarrow (T_f - 28°C) = \dfrac{15\ J}{12\ g \times \dfrac{0.449\ J}{g\ °C}} \Rightarrow$

$T_f = 2.78 + 28°C = 31\ °C$

69. $248 \, cal \times \dfrac{4.184 \, J}{1 \, cal} = 24 \, g \times \dfrac{4.18 \, J}{g \, ^{\circ}C} \times (\Delta T) \Rightarrow \Delta T = \dfrac{1037.6}{100.3} = 1.0 \times 10^{1} \, ^{\circ}C$

71. $58 \, J = 28 \, g \times (\text{heat capacity}) \times (39.9 - 31.1)^{\circ}C \Rightarrow$

$\text{heat capacity} = \dfrac{58 \, J}{(28 \, g)(8.8 \, ^{\circ}C)} = 0.24 \dfrac{J}{g \, ^{\circ}C}$

$\therefore$ It is consistent with silver metal

73. $56 \, J = 11 \, g \times (\text{heat capacity}) \times (12.7 - 10.4)^{\circ}C \Rightarrow$

$\text{heat capacity} = \dfrac{56 \, J}{(11g)(2.3 \, ^{\circ}C)} = 2.2 \dfrac{J}{g \, ^{\circ}C}$

Cumulative Problems

75. $17 \, kJ \times \dfrac{1000 \, J}{1 \, kJ} = 245g \times \dfrac{4.18 \, J}{g \, ^{\circ}C} \times (T_f - 32 ^{\circ}C) \Rightarrow$

$(T_f - 32 ^{\circ}C) = \dfrac{1.7 \times 10^{4} \, J}{245g \times \dfrac{4.18 \, J}{g \, ^{\circ}C}} \Rightarrow T_f = 16.6 + 32 ^{\circ}C = 49 \, ^{\circ}C$

* Assume 1 mL of water is equal to 1 gram.

77. $\text{Heat} = 1.57 \, cm^3 \times \dfrac{19.3 \, g}{1 \, cm^3} \times \dfrac{0.128 \, J}{g \, ^{\circ}C} \times (29.5 - 11.4 ^{\circ}C) = 70.2 \, J$

79. $kJ = 56 \, L \times \dfrac{1000 \, mL}{1 \, L} \times \dfrac{1 \, g}{1 \, mL} \times \dfrac{4.18 \, J}{g \, ^{\circ}C} \times 71 ^{\circ}C^{*} \times \dfrac{1 \, kJ}{1000 \, J} = 1.7 \times 10^{4} \, kJ$

You must convert each temperature prior to taking the difference.

$T_f = (212 ^{\circ}F - 32) \times \dfrac{5}{9} = 100 ^{\circ}C; \qquad T_i = (85 ^{\circ}F - 32) \times \dfrac{5}{9} = 29 ^{\circ}C$

$\Delta T = 100 ^{\circ}C - 29 ^{\circ}C = 71 ^{\circ}C$

81. $2.3 \text{ kWh} \times \dfrac{3.60 \times 10^6 \text{ J}}{1 \text{ kWh}} = 29.5 \text{ L} \times \dfrac{1000 \text{ mL}}{1 \text{ L}} \times \dfrac{1 \text{ g}}{1 \text{ ml}} \times \dfrac{4.18 \text{ J}}{\text{g °C}} \times \Delta T \;\Rightarrow$

$$\Delta T = \dfrac{2.3 \text{ kWh} \times \dfrac{3.60 \times 10^6 \text{ J}}{1 \text{ kWh}}}{29.5 \text{ L} \times \dfrac{1000 \text{ mL}}{1 \text{ L}} \times \dfrac{1 \text{ g}}{1 \text{ ml}} \times \dfrac{4.18 \text{ J}}{\text{g °C}}} = \dfrac{8.28 \times 10^6}{1.045 \times 10^5} = 67 °C$$

83. $\text{kWh} = 55 \text{ gal} \times \dfrac{3.785 \text{ L}}{1 \text{ gal}} \times \dfrac{1000 \text{ mL}}{1 \text{ L}} \times \dfrac{1 \text{ g}}{1 \text{ mL}} \times \dfrac{4.18 \text{ J}}{\text{g °C}} \times 25 °C \times \dfrac{1 \text{ kWh}}{3.60 \times 10^6 \text{ J}}$

$= 6.0 \text{ kWh}$

85. $\text{kJ} = 2.5 \text{ kg} \times \dfrac{1000 \text{ g}}{1 \text{ kg}} \times \dfrac{4.18 \text{ J}}{\text{g °C}} \times (100.0 - 25) °C \times \dfrac{1 \text{ kJ}}{1000 \text{ J}} = 7.8 \times 10^2 \text{ kJ}$

$\text{grams of fuel} = \dfrac{7.8 \times 10^2 \text{ kJ}}{\left(\dfrac{36 \text{ kJ}}{\text{g}} \right)} = 22 \text{ grams}$

87. a) pure substance
    b) pure substance
    c) pure substance
    d) mixture

89. physical change

Highlight Problems

91. The weather patterns that develop over the ocean exchange heat with the water. If the water is several degrees colder than the air above it, an extremely large amount of heat is removed from the air to the water. This is because water has a large heat capacity and air has a low heat capacity. Conversely, if the water is several degrees warmer than the air above it, a tremendous amount of heat can be transferred to the air. This occurs all of the time and is part of our normal weather patterns. However, during the El Niño/La Niña cycle, this heat transfer to and from water and air increases dramatically, which is why it alters weather patterns on a global scale.

93. a) San Francisco is nearly surrounded by the ocean. Because water can absorb large amounts of heat without a increase temperature (i.e. water has a large heat capacity), San Francisco enjoys moderate temperatures. Sacramento, on the other hand, is a land-locked city. The earth has a relatively low heat capacity, which means that as the earth absorbs heat, the temperature quickly increases (i.e. a small heat capacity).

b) In the winter, San Francisco is a warmer place. The ocean releases a large amount of heat back into the colder atmosphere because it can store a tremendous amount of heat. Sacramento, on the other hand, is surrounded by land and is cooler because the earth's heat capacity is much lower than the ocean's.

Atoms and Elements

4

Questions

1. The atom is the basic building block of all matter; by understanding the atom, we gain important insights into the properties of all matter.

3. Democritus reasoned that matter was made of small, indivisible, indestructible particles.

5. Rutherford had shot alpha particles at an extremely thin gold foil target. The majority of alpha particles pass directly through the foil, some particles were slightly deflected and 1 in 20,000 bounced back toward the alpha source. If the plum pudding model were correct, the only result would have been a slight deflection of some of the particles.

7.

Particle	Mass (kg)	Mass (amu)	Charge	Location
Proton	1.67262×10^{-27}	1	+1	Inside Nucleus
Neutron	1.67493×10^{-27}	1	0	Inside Nucleus
Electron	0.00091×10^{-27}	0.00055	$^-1$	Outside Nucleus

9. Matter is usually charge neutral because the protons and electrons cancel each other and when an imbalance does exist, it usually corrects itself very soon.

11. A chemical symbol is a one or two letter abbreviation that is unique to each element.

13. Mendeleev was the first person to organize the elements into what we would recognize as a version of the modern periodic table. Mendeleev based his table on increasing molecular mass of elements and grouping elements with similar properties into columns.

15. The modern periodic table is organized by increasing atomic number, which is the number of protons found in each element.

17. The properties of nonmetals are: (1) poor conductors of heat and electricity (2) tend to gain electrons in reactions (3) can be found as solids, liquids, or gases. Nonmetals make up the upper right side of the periodic table.

19. A family or group of elements is the term given to the column on a periodic table which all have similar, periodic properties.

21. An ion is an atom that becomes electrically charged due the gain/loss of electrons.

23. a) +1   b) +2   c) +3   d) $^-2$
    e) $^-1$

25. The percent natural abundance of isotopes provides the relative amounts of each isotope found in a sample of the element. These numbers are constant no matter the source of the element and are unique to each different element.

27. The first method for specifying isotopes is to superscript and subscript the mass number and atomic number, respectively, on the left side of the chemical symbol (e.g., $_1^2H$). The second method is to identify the element followed by the mass number (e.g., H-2 or hydrogen-2).

Atomic and Nuclear Theory

29. a) consistent; all atoms of a given element have the same mass and other properties that distinguish it from the atoms of other elements.
   b) inconsistent; each element is composed of tiny indestructible particles called atoms.
   c) inconsistent; atoms combine in simple, whole-number ratios to form compounds.
   d) consistent; atoms combine in simple, whole-number ratios to form compounds.

31. a) consistent; there are as many negatively charged electrons outside the nucleus as there are positively charged particles (called protons) inside the nucleus, therefore the atom is electrically neutral.
   b) inconsistent; most of the volume of the atom is empty space occupied by tiny, negatively charged electrons.
   c) inconsistent; there are as many negatively charged electrons outside the nucleus as there are positively charged particles (called protons) inside the nucleus, therefore the atom is electrically neutral.
   d) inconsistent; most of the atom's mass and all of its positive charge are contained in a small core called the nucleus.

Protons, Neutrons, and Electrons

33. a) True
   b) True
   c) False
   d) True

35. a) False
    b) True
    c) False
    d) True

37. (Mass of 1 Electron)(X)=(Mass of 1 Proton) $\Rightarrow$

$$X = \frac{\text{(Mass of 1 Proton)}}{\text{(Mass of 1 Electron)}} = \frac{1.67262 \times 10^{-27}}{0.00091 \times 10^{-27}} = 1.8 \times 10^3$$

Elements, Symbols, and Names

39. a) 27
    b) 77
    c) 92
    d) 14
    e) 4

41. a) 25
    b) 47
    c) 79
    d) 82
    e) 16

43. a) C, 6
    b) N, 7
    c) Na, 11
    d) K, 19
    e) Cu, 29

45. a) Gold, 79
    b) Silicon, 14
    c) Nickel, 28
    d) Zinc, 30
    e) Tungsten, 74

47.

Element Name	Element Symbol	Atomic Number
silver	Ag	47
gallium	Ga	31
arsenic	As	33
astatine	At	85

The Periodic Table

49. a) metal b) metal c) non-metal d) nonmetal e) metalloid

51. Metals lose electrons in reactions ∴ a) potassium, d) barium and e) copper

53. a) Te and b) K

55. c) calcium and d) barium

57. a) sodium, b) potassium, and e) cesium

59. a) halogen b) noble gas c) halogen d) neither e) noble gas

61. a) 6A b) 3A c) 4A d) 4A e) 5A

63. The elements most like sulfur would be those elements in the same group (6A) because they all have similar physical and chemical properties. Therefore, the answer is b) oxygen.

65. The elements that come from the same group would be the most similar because they have similar chemical and physical properties. Therefore, the answer is b) Cl and F.

67.

Chemical Symbol	Group Number	Group Name	Metal or Nonmetal
Na	1A	alkali metal	metal
He	8A	noble gas	nonmetal
I	7A	halogen	nonmetal
Sr	2A	alkaline earth	metal

Ions

69. a) $Na \rightarrow Na^+ + \underline{e^-}$
b) $O + 2\,e^- \rightarrow \underline{O^{-2}}$
c) $Ca \rightarrow Ca^{+2} + \underline{2e^-}$
d) $Cl + e^- \rightarrow \underline{Cl^-}$

71. a) oxygen ion charge = 8 (+1) + 10 (-1) = -2
b) aluminum ion charge = 13 (+1) + 10 (-1) = +3
c) titanium ion charge = 22 (+1) + 18 (-1) = +4
d) iodine ion charge = 53 (+1) + 54 (-1) = -1

73. a) Potassium has 19 protons, therefore the +1 ion has 18 electrons.
    b) Sulfur has 16 protons, therefore the -2 ion has 18 electrons.
    c) Strontium has 38 protons, therefore the +2 ion has 36 electrons.
    d) Chromium has 24 protons, therefore the +3 ion has 21 electrons.

75. a) False; The Ti^{+2} ion contains 22 protons and 20 electrons.
    b) True
    c) False; The Mg^{+2} ion contains 12 protons and 10 electrons.
    d) True

77. a) Rb is in group 1A, therefore it will form Rb^+.
    b) K is in group 1A, therefore it will form K^+.
    c) Al in group 3A, therefore it will form Al^{+3}.
    d) O is in group 6A, therefore it will form O^{-2}.

79. a) Ga is in group 3A, therefore it will lose 3 electrons.
    b) Li is in group 1A, therefore it will lose 1 electron.
    c) Br is in group 7A, therefore it will gain 1 electron.
    d) S is in group 6A, therefore it will gain 2 electrons.

81.

Symbol	Ion Formed	# electrons in ion	# protons in ion
Ca	Ca^{+2}	<u>18</u>	<u>20</u>
Te	Te^{-2}	54	<u>52</u>
In	In^{+3}	<u>46</u>	49
<u>Sr</u>	Sr^{+2}	36	38

Isotopes

83. a) Z=1, A=2
    b) Z=24, A=51
    c) Z=20, A=40
    d) Z=73, A=181

85. a) $^{16}_{8}O$

    b) $^{19}_{9}F$

    c) $^{23}_{11}Na$

    d) $^{27}_{13}Al$

87. a) $_{27}^{60}\text{Co}$

b) $_{10}^{22}\text{Ne}$

c) $_{53}^{131}\text{I}$

d) $_{94}^{244}\text{Pu}$

89. a) protons = Z = 11, neutrons = A-Z = 23-11 = 12
b) protons = Z = 88, neutrons = A-Z = 266-88 = 178
c) protons = Z = 82, neutrons = A-Z = 208-82 = 126
d) protons = Z = 7, neutrons = A-Z = 14-7 = 7

91. Carbon-14 has Z=6, therefore, protons = Z = 6, and neutrons = A–Z= 14-6 = 8. The correct isotope symbol would be $_{6}^{14}\text{C}$.

Atomic Mass

93. Calculating the atomic mass of an element involves taking a weighted average in which you multiply the percent natural abundance by the atomic mass for each isotope and then add these products together. For rubidium: (0.7217)(84.9118)+(.2783)(86.9092) = 85.46 amu.

95. a) 100–50.69 = 49.31%
b) (0.5069)(mass)+(0.4931)(80.9163) = 79.904 ⇒ Mass = (79.904–39.90)/0.5069
   ⇒Mass = 40.00/0.5069 = 78.92 amu

97. MW = (0.574)(120.9038) + (0.426)(122.9042) ⇒ MW = 69.4 + 52.4 = 121.8
The atomic weight is closest to that of antimony (Sb) which is 121.760 amu.

Cumulative Problems

99. $-125 \text{ mC} \times \dfrac{1 \text{ C}}{1000 \text{ mC}} \times \dfrac{1 \text{ e}^-}{-1.6 \times 10^{-19} \text{ C}} = 7.8 \times 10^{17} \text{e}^-$

101.

Symbol	#p	#n	A (Mass Number)	Natural Abundance
Sr-84 or $^{84}_{38}$Sr	38	46	84	0.56%
Sr-86 or $^{86}_{38}$Sr	38	48	86	9.86%
Sr-87 or $^{87}_{38}$Sr	38	49	87	7.00%
Sr-88 or $^{88}_{38}$Sr	38	50	88	82.58%

Atomic Mass of Sr is the weighted average of each isotope:

$Sr=(0.0056 \times 83.9134)+(0.0986 \times 85.9093)+(0.0700 \times 86.9089)+$

(0.8258×87.9056)

$Sr=0.47+8.47+6.08+72.59=87.62$ amu

103.

Symbol	Z	A	#p	#e$^-$	#n	Charge
Fe	26	58	26	24	32	+2
Cu	29	53	29	27	24	+2
P	15	31	15	15	16	0
O	8	16	8	10	8	$^-$2

105. $100-47.8=52.2\%$

$(.478)(150.9198) + (.522)(Eu-153) = 151.964 \Rightarrow$

$Eu-153 = (151.964 - 72.1)/(0.522) \Rightarrow$

$Eu-153 =79.9/0.522 = 152.996 \Rightarrow 153$ amu

Highlight Problems

107. a) Nt-304: $\dfrac{36}{50} \times 100\% = 72\%$

Nt-305: $\dfrac{2}{50} \times 100\% = 4.0\%$

Nt-306: $\dfrac{12}{50} \times 100\% = 24\%$

b) MW of Nt = (0.72)(303.956)+(0.040)(304.962)+(0.24)(305.978)

=304.482 (the percentages are exact, countable numbers).

Molecules and Compounds

5

Questions

1. The properties of an element completely change when it combines with another element to form a compound. For example, water is made out of the elements hydrogen and oxygen, both of which are gases. When hydrogen and oxygen combine to form water, their properties and they become a new liquid substance.

3. The law of constant composition was first expressed by Joseph Proust states: All samples of a given compound have the same proportions of their constituent elements.

5. The general rule for listing elements in a compound is that the most metallic element is listed first. For compounds which contain a metal, it is listed first. For compounds that do not contain a metal, the most metal-like element is listed first. For nonmetals, you list the element that is found farthest to the left and/or the element that is lowest on the periodic table.

7. Most elements can be found in nature as single atoms, which we call the **atomic elements**. However, some elements can only be found in nature in the diatomic state, that is two atoms of the same element bonded together which we call the **molecular elements**. There are only 7 diatomic molecular elements: hydrogen (H_2), nitrogen (N_2), oxygen (O_2), fluorine (F_2), chlorine (Cl_2), bromine (Br_2), and iodine (I_2). *It is tradition that when a chemists says a molecular elements by name, they are referring to the diatomic state. When your instructor says oxygen reacts with hydrogen, you know to write O_2 and H_2. A reaction that involves just a single atom of these molecular elements you say monatomic oxygen (O).*

9. The systematic name for a compound will provide the reader with enough information that the formula of the compound can be determined. The common name can be considered a "nickname" for the compound that everybody automatically knows.

11. The metals that form Type II Ionic Compounds are most commonly found in the center section of the periodic table, known as the transition metals.

5

13. The basic form for naming Type II Binary compounds is the same as Type I with the addition of the charge of the cation, written in roman numerals, inserted in parentheses between the cation name and the anion name. The pattern is: [Cation Name](cation charge-roman numerals) [Anion Base Name + -ide]

15. When you name compounds that contain polyatomic ions, you use the same rules from Type I and Type II, however, you insert the name of the polyatomic ions, without altering the name, into their proper place.

17. The basic form for naming molecular compounds is [prefix-1st element][prefix-2nd element].

19. The basic form for naming binary acids is: [hydro+base nonmetal name+ "ic"][acid].

21. The basic form for naming oxyanions with the "-ite" ending is: [base oxyanion name+"ous"][acid].

Problems

Constant Composition of Compounds

23. Sample 1: $\dfrac{\text{mass Cl}}{\text{mass Na}} = \dfrac{7.16}{4.65} = 1.54$

    Sample 2: $\dfrac{\text{mass Cl}}{\text{mass Na}} = \dfrac{11.5}{7.45} = 1.54$, Yes

25. Sample 1: $\dfrac{\text{mass F}}{\text{mass Mg}} = \dfrac{2.57}{1.65} = 1.56$

    Sample 2: $\dfrac{\text{mass F}}{\text{mass Mg}} = \dfrac{\text{mass F}}{1.32} = 1.56$

    mass F $= 1.56 \times 1.32 = 2.06$ kg

Chemical Formulas

27. NBr_3

29. a) Fe_2O_3
    b) PCl_3
    c) PCl_5
    d) Ag_2O

31. a) 4
    b) 4
    c) 2×3=6
    d) 2×2=4

33. a) Mg=1, Cl=2
    b) Na=1, N=1, O=3
    c) Ca=1, N=2×1=2, O=2×2=4
    d) Sr=1, O=2×1=2, H=2×1=2

Molecular View of Elements and Compounds

35. a) atomic
    b) molecular
    c) molecular
    d) atomic

37. a) molecular
    b) ionic
    c) ionic
    d) molecular

39. Helium — single atoms,
    CCl_4 — molecules
    K_2SO_4 — Formula units
    bromine — diatomic molecules

41. a) formula units
    b) single atoms
    c) molecules
    d) molecules

43. a) ionic, Type I
    b) molecular
    c) molecular
    d) ionic, Type II

Writing Formulas for Ionic Compounds

45. a) Sr =+2, O =⁻2: SrO
    b) Na=+1, O=⁻2: Na_2O
    c) Al=+3, S=⁻2: Al_2S_3
    d) Sr=+2, Br=⁻1: $SrBr_2$

47. a) $KC_2H_3O_2$
    b) K_2CrO_4
    c) K_3PO_4
    d) KCN

49. N=$^-$3, O=$^-$2, F=$^-$1
    a) K=+1: K_3N, K_2O, KF
    b) Ba=+2: Ba_3N_2, BaO, BaF_2
    c) Al=+3: AlN, Al_2O_3, AlF_3

Naming Ionic Compounds

51. a) cesium chloride
    b) strontium bromide
    c) potassium oxide
    d) lithium fluoride

53. a) chromium (II) chloride
    b) chromium (III) chloride
    c) tin (IV) oxide
    d) lead (II) iodide

55. a) Type II, chromium (III) oxide
    b) Type I, sodium iodide
    c) Type I, calcium bromide
    d) Type II, tin (II) oxide

57. a) barium nitrate
    b) lead (II) acetate
    c) ammonium iodide
    d) potassium chlorate
    e) cobalt (II) sulfate
    f) sodium perchlorate

59. a) $CuBr_2$
    b) $AgNO_3$
    c) KOH
    d) Na_2SO_4
    e) $KHSO_4$
    f) $NaHCO_3$

Naming Molecular Compounds

61. a) sulfur dioxide
    b) nitrogen triiodide
    c) bromine pentafluoride
    d) nitrogen monoxide
    e) tetranitrogen tetraselenide

63. a) CO
    b) S_2F_4
    c) Cl_2O
    d) PF_5
    e) BBr_3
    f) P_2S_5

65. a) incorrect, phosphorus pentabromide
    b) incorrect, diphosphorus trioxide
    c) incorrrect, sulfur tetrafluoride
    d) correct

67. a) chlorous acid
    b) hydroiodic acid
    c) sulfuric acid
    d) nitric acid

69. a) H_3PO_4
    b) HBr
    c) H_2SO_3

Formula Mass

71. a) FM=1.008+14.01+2(16.00)=47.02 amu
    b) FM=40.08+2(35.45)=110.98 amu
    c) FM=12.01+4(35.45)=153.81 amu
    d) FM=24.31+2(14.01)+6(16.00)=148.33 amu

73. PBr_3(FM=270.67) > Ag_2O(FM=231.8) > PtO_2(FM=227.1) > $Al(NO_3)_3$(FM=213.01)

75. a) ionic, cobalt (III) cyanide
    b) acid, chromic acid
    c) ionic, potassium chloride
    d) molecular, dihydrogen terahydride

77. a) incorrect, calcium nitrite
    b) incorrect, potassium oxide
    c) incorrect, phosphorus trichloride
    d) correct

79. a) $Sn(SO_4)_2$, FM=118.7+2(32.06)+8(16.00)=310.8 amu
    b) HNO_2, FM=1.008+14.01+2(16.00)=47.02 amu
    c) $NaHCO_3$, FM=22.99+1.008+12.01+3(16.00)=84.01 amu
    d) PF_5, FM=30.97+5(19.00)=125.97 amu

81. a) platinum (IV) oxide, FM=195.1+2(16.00)=227.1 amu
    b) dinitrogen pentoxide, FM=2(14.01)+5(16.00)=108.02 amu
    c) aluminum chlorate, FM=26.98+3(35.45)+9(16.00)=277.33 amu
    d) phosphorus pentabromide, FM=30.97+5(79.90)=430.47 amu

Highlight Problems

83. a) molecular element
    b) atomic element
    c) ionic compound
    d) molecular compound

85. Image 1: sodium hypochlorite: $NaClO$, sodium hydroxide: $NaOH$
    Image 2: calcium carbonate: $CaCO_3$
    Image 3: sodium bicarbonate: $NaHCO_3$
    Image 4: sodium bicarbonate: $NaHCO_3$, calcium carbonate: $CaCO_3$,
             calcium phosphate: $Ca_3(PO_4)_2$, sodium aluminum sulfate: $NaAl(SO_4)_2$

Chemical Composition   6 _____

Questions

1. Chemical composition is important to understand because it provides an analysis of the amount of an element found within a compound.

3. There are 6.022×10^{23} atoms in 1 mole of atoms.

5. One mole of atoms of an element has a mass in grams that is equal to the mass of the atom in atomic mass units (amu).

7. a) 30.97 g   b) 195.08 g   c) 12.01 g   d) 52.00 g

9. The subscripts provide a ratio of atoms of one element to atoms of another element within a compound. This ratio does not apply to mass because every element has a different mass. A one-to-one atomic ratio for hydrogen to oxygen is very different than the one-to-one atomic ratio for hydrogen to sulfur because sulfur has a mass of over twice the mass of oxygen.

11. a) 11.19 g H ≡ 100 g water
    b) 53.29 g O ≡ 100 g fructose
    c) 84.12 g C ≡ 100 g gasoline
    d) 52.14 g C ≡ 100 g ethanol

13. The molecular formula is a whole-number multiple of the empirical formula.

15. The empirical formula mass is the sum of the masses of all atoms found in the simplest whole-number ratio of each atom type found in a compound.

The Mole Concept

17. $5.9 \text{ mol Hg} \times \dfrac{6.022 \times 10^{23} \text{ Hg atoms}}{1 \text{ mole of Hg atoms}} = 3.6 \times 10^{24} \text{ atoms}$

31

19. a) $3.4 \text{ mol Cu} \times \dfrac{6.022 \times 10^{23} \text{ Cu atoms}}{1 \text{ mole Cu}} = 2.0 \times 10^{24} \text{ Cu atoms}$

b) $9.7 \times 10^{-3} \text{ mol C} \times \dfrac{6.022 \times 10^{23} \text{ C atoms}}{1 \text{ mole C}} = 5.8 \times 10^{21} \text{ C atoms}$

c) $22.9 \text{ mol Hg} \times \dfrac{6.022 \times 10^{23} \text{ Hg atoms}}{1 \text{ mole Hg}} = 1.38 \times 10^{25} \text{ Hg atoms}$

d) $0.215 \text{ mol Na} \times \dfrac{6.022 \times 10^{23} \text{ Na atoms}}{1 \text{ mole Na}} = 1.29 \times 10^{23} \text{ Na atoms}$

21. a) $872 \text{ sheets} \times \dfrac{1 \text{ dozen}}{12 \text{ sheets}} = 72.7 \text{ dozen}$

b) $872 \text{ sheets} \times \dfrac{1 \text{ gross}}{144 \text{ sheets}} = 6.06 \text{ gross}$

c) $872 \text{ sheets} \times \dfrac{1 \text{ ream}}{500 \text{ sheets}} = 1.74 \text{ reams}$

d) $872 \text{ sheets} \times \dfrac{1 \text{ mole}}{6.022 \times 10^{23} \text{ sheets}} = 1.45 \times 10^{-21} \text{ moles}$

23. $42.3 \text{ g Sn} \times \dfrac{1 \text{ mole Sn}}{118.7 \text{ g Sn}} = 0.356 \text{ mole Sn}$

25. a) $1.54 \text{ g Zn} \times \dfrac{1 \text{ mole Zn}}{65.39 \text{ g Zn}} = 2.36 \times 10^{-2} \text{ mole Zn}$

b) $22.8 \text{ g Ar} \times \dfrac{1 \text{ mole Ar}}{39.95 \text{ g Ar}} = 0.571 \text{ mole Ar}$

c) $86.2 \text{ g Ta} \times \dfrac{1 \text{ mole Ta}}{180.9 \text{ g Ta}} = 0.477 \text{ mole Ta}$

d) $0.034 \text{ g Li} \times \dfrac{1 \text{ mole Li}}{6.941 \text{ g Li}} = 4.9 \times 10^{-3} \text{ mole Li}$

27. $0.0134 \text{ mmol Ag} \times \dfrac{1 \times 10^{-3} \text{ mole Ag}}{1 \text{ mmole Ag}} \times \dfrac{6.022 \times 10^{23} \text{ Ag atoms}}{1 \text{ mole Ag}}$

$= 8.07 \times 10^{18} \text{ Ag atoms}$

29. $3.78 \text{ g Al} \times \dfrac{1 \text{ mole Al}}{26.98 \text{ g Al}} \times \dfrac{6.022 \times 10^{23} \text{ Al atoms}}{1 \text{ mole Al}} = 8.44 \times 10^{22} \text{ Al atoms}$

31. a) $12.8\text{g Sr} \times \dfrac{1 \text{ mol Sr}}{87.62 \text{ g Sr}} \times \dfrac{6.022 \times 10^{23} \text{ Sr atoms}}{1 \text{ mol Sr}} = 8.80 \times 10^{22} \text{ Sr atoms}$

b) $45.2\text{g Fe} \times \dfrac{1 \text{ mol Fe}}{55.85\text{g Fe}} \times \dfrac{6.022 \times 10^{23} \text{ Fe atoms}}{1 \text{ mol Fe}} = 4.87 \times 10^{23} \text{ Fe atoms}$

c) $9.87\text{g Bi} \times \dfrac{1 \text{ mol Bi}}{209.0\text{g Bi}} \times \dfrac{6.022 \times 10^{23} \text{ Bi atoms}}{1 \text{ mol Bi}} = 2.84 \times 10^{22} \text{ Bi atoms}$

d) $36.1 \text{ g P} \times \dfrac{1 \text{ mole P}}{30.97 \text{ g P}} \times \dfrac{6.022 \times 10^{23} \text{ P atoms}}{1 \text{ mole P}} = 7.02 \times 10^{23} \text{ P atoms}$

33. $52\text{mg C} \times \dfrac{1 \text{ g}}{1000\text{mg}} \times \dfrac{1 \text{ mol C}}{12.01\text{g C}} \times \dfrac{6.022 \times 10^{23} \text{ atoms}}{1 \text{ mol C}} = 2.6 \times 10^{21} \text{ C atoms}$

35. $1.28 \text{ kg Ti} \times \dfrac{1 \times 10^{3} \text{ g}}{1 \text{ kg}} \times \dfrac{1 \text{ mole Ti}}{47.88 \text{ g Ti}} \times \dfrac{6.022 \times 10^{23} \text{ Ti atoms}}{1 \text{ mole Ti}} = 1.61 \times 10^{25} \text{ He atoms}$

37. $1.32 \text{ g C}_{10}\text{H}_{8} \times \dfrac{1 \text{ mole C}_{10}\text{H}_{8}}{128.16 \text{ g C}_{10}\text{H}_{8}} \times \dfrac{6.022 \times 10^{23} \text{ C}_{10}\text{H}_{8} \text{ molecules}}{1 \text{ mole C}_{10}\text{H}_{8}} \Rightarrow$

$= 6.20 \times 10^{21} \text{ C}_{10}\text{H}_{8} \text{ molecules}$

39. a) $3.5 \text{ g } H_2O \times \dfrac{1 \text{ mole } H_2O}{18.02 \text{ g}} \times \dfrac{6.022 \times 10^{23} \text{ molecules}}{1 \text{ mole } H_2O} = 1.2 \times 10^{23} H_2O$ molecules

b) $56.1 \text{g } N_2 \times \dfrac{1 \text{ mole } N_2}{28.02 \text{ g}} \times \dfrac{6.022 \times 10^{23} \text{ molecules}}{1 \text{ mole } N_2} = 1.21 \times 10^{24} N_2$ molecules

c) $89 \text{g } CCl_4 \times \dfrac{1 \text{ mole } CCl_4}{153.81 \text{ g}} \times \dfrac{6.022 \times 10^{23} \text{ molecules}}{1 \text{ mole } CCl_4} = 3.5 \times 10^{23} CCl_4$ molecules

d) $19 \text{g } C_6H_{12}O_6 \times \dfrac{1 \text{ mole } C_6H_{12}O_6}{180.16 \text{ g}} \times \dfrac{6.022 \times 10^{23} \text{ molecules}}{1 \text{ mole } C_6H_{12}O_6} \Rightarrow$

$= 6.4 \times 10^{22} C_6H_{12}O_6$ molecules

41. $1.8 \times 10^{17} C_{12}H_{22}O_{11}$ molecules $\times \dfrac{1 \text{ mole } C_{12}H_{22}O_{11}}{6.022 \times 10^{23} \text{ molecules}} \times \dfrac{342.30 \text{ g}}{1 \text{ mole } C_{12}H_{22}O_{11}} \times$

$\dfrac{1000 \text{ mg}}{1 \text{ g}} = 0.10 \text{ mg } C_{12}H_{22}O_{11}$

Chemical Formulas as Conversion Factors

43. $4.7 \text{ moles } CaCl_2 \times \dfrac{2 \text{ moles } Cl}{1 \text{ mole } CaCl_2} = 9.4 \text{ moles } Cl$

45. a) $2.3 \text{ moles } H_2O \times \dfrac{1 \text{ mole } O}{1 \text{ mole } H_2O} = 2.3 \text{ moles } O$

b) $1.2 \text{ moles } H_2O_2 \times \dfrac{2 \text{ mole } O}{1 \text{ mole } H_2O_2} = 2.4 \text{ moles } O$

c) $0.9 \text{ moles } NaNO_3 \times \dfrac{3 \text{ mole } O}{1 \text{ mole } NaNO_3} = 2.7 \text{ moles } O$

d) $0.5 \text{ moles } Ca(NO_3)_2 \times \dfrac{6 \text{ mole } O}{1 \text{ mole } Ca(NO_3)_2} = 3.0 \text{ moles } O$

The correct answer is d).

47. a) $3.8 \text{ moles } CH_4 \times \dfrac{1 \text{ mole C}}{1 \text{ mole } CH_4} = 3.8 \text{ moles C}$

 b) $0.273 \text{ moles } C_2H_6 \times \dfrac{2 \text{ mole C}}{1 \text{ mole } C_2H_6} = 0.546 \text{ moles C}$

 c) $4.89 \text{ moles } C_4H_{10} \times \dfrac{4 \text{ mole C}}{1 \text{ mole } C_4H_{10}} = 19.6 \text{ moles C}$

 d) $22.9 \text{ moles } C_8H_{18} \times \dfrac{8 \text{ mole C}}{1 \text{ mole } C_8H_{18}} = 183 \text{ moles C}$

49. a) $55 \text{ g } CF_2Cl_2 \times \dfrac{1 \text{ mol } CF_2Cl_2}{120.91 \text{ g}} \times \dfrac{2 \text{ mol Cl}}{1 \text{ mol } CF_2Cl_2} \times \dfrac{35.45 \text{ g}}{1 \text{ mol Cl}} = 32 \text{ g Cl}$

 b) $55 \text{ g } CFCl_3 \times \dfrac{1 \text{ mol } CFCl_3}{137.36 \text{ g}} \times \dfrac{3 \text{ mol Cl}}{1 \text{ mol } CFCl_3} \times \dfrac{35.45 \text{ g}}{1 \text{ mol Cl}} = 43 \text{ g Cl}$

 c) $55 \text{ g } C_2F_3Cl_3 \times \dfrac{1 \text{ mol } C_2F_3Cl_3}{187.37 \text{ g}} \times \dfrac{3 \text{ mol Cl}}{1 \text{ mol } C_2F_3Cl_3} \times \dfrac{35.45 \text{ g}}{1 \text{ mol Cl}} = 31 \text{ g Cl}$

 d) $55 \text{ g } CF_3Cl \times \dfrac{1 \text{ mol } CF_3Cl}{104.46 \text{ g}} \times \dfrac{1 \text{ mol Cl}}{1 \text{ mol } CF_3Cl} \times \dfrac{35.45 \text{ g}}{1 \text{ mol Cl}} = 19 \text{ g Cl}$

51. a) $1.0 \times 10^3 \text{kg Fe} \times \dfrac{1000 \text{g}}{1 \text{ kg}} \times \dfrac{1 \text{mol Fe}}{55.85 \text{ g}} \times \dfrac{1 \text{ mol } Fe_2O_3}{2 \text{ mol Fe}} \times \dfrac{159.70 \text{ g}}{1 \text{ mol } Fe_2O_3} \times \dfrac{1 \text{ kg}}{1 \times 10^3 \text{g}}$

 $= 1.4 \times 10^3 \text{ kg } Fe_2O_3$

 b) $1.0 \times 10^3 \text{kg Fe} \times \dfrac{1 \times 10^3 \text{g}}{1 \text{ kg}} \times \dfrac{1 \text{ mol Fe}}{55.85 \text{ g}} \times \dfrac{1 \text{ mol } Fe_3O_4}{3 \text{ mol Fe}} \times \dfrac{231.55 \text{ g}}{1 \text{ mol } Fe_3O_4} \times$

 $\dfrac{1 \text{ kg}}{1 \times 10^3 \text{g}} = 1.4 \times 10^3 \text{ kg } Fe_3O_4$

 c) $1.0 \times 10^3 \text{kg Fe} \times \dfrac{1 \times 10^3 \text{g}}{1 \text{ kg}} \times \dfrac{1 \text{ mol Fe}}{55.85 \text{ g}} \times \dfrac{1 \text{ mol } FeCO_3}{1 \text{ mol Fe}} \times \dfrac{115.86 \text{ g}}{1 \text{ mol } FeCO_3} \times$

 $\dfrac{1 \text{ kg}}{1 \times 10^3 \text{g}} = 2.1 \times 10^3 \text{ kg } FeCO_3$

Mass Percent Composition

53. mass % Sr$=\dfrac{2.45 \text{ g Sr}}{2.89 \text{ g SrO}}\times100\%=84.8\%$ Sr

55. mass % Ca$=\dfrac{0.690 \text{ g Ca}}{1.912 \text{ g CaCl}_2}\times100\%=36.1\%$ Ca

mass % Cl$=\dfrac{1.222 \text{ g Cl}}{1.912 \text{ g CaCl}_2}\times100\%=63.9\%$ Cl

57. $\dfrac{\text{mass F}}{28.5\text{g CuF}_2}\times100\%=37.42\%$ F $\Rightarrow$ mass F$=\dfrac{(37.42\% \text{ F})(28.5\text{g CuF}_2)}{100\%}=10.7$g

59. $\dfrac{3 \text{ mg F}}{\text{mass NaF}}\times100\%=45.24\%$ F $\Rightarrow$ mass NaF$=\dfrac{(3 \text{ mg F})(100\%)}{45.24\% \text{ F}}=7$ mg NaF

Mass Percent Composition From Chemical Formula

61. Assume one mole of each compound and determine the mass % using molar masses.

a) mass % N$=\dfrac{28.02 \text{ g N}}{44.02 \text{ g N}_2\text{O}}\times100\%=63.65\%$ N

b) mass % N$=\dfrac{14.01 \text{ g N}}{30.01 \text{ g NO}}\times100\% = 46.68\%$ N

c) mass % N$=\dfrac{14.01 \text{ g N}}{46.01 \text{ g NO}_2}\times100\% = 30.45\%$ N

d) mass % N$=\dfrac{28.02 \text{ g N}}{108.02 \text{ g N}_2\text{O}_5}\times100\% = 25.94\%$ N

63. Assume 1 mole of each compound, base mass % from molar masses.

a) mass % C = $\dfrac{24.02 \text{ g C}}{60.05 \text{ g C}_2\text{H}_4\text{O}_2} \times 100\% = 40.00\%$ C

mass % H = $\dfrac{4.032 \text{ g H}}{60.05 \text{ g C}_2\text{H}_4\text{O}_2} \times 100\% = 6.714\%$ H

mass % O = $\dfrac{32.00 \text{ g O}}{60.05 \text{ g C}_2\text{H}_4\text{O}_2} \times 100\% = 53.29\%$ O

b) mass % C = $\dfrac{12.01 \text{ g C}}{46.03 \text{ g CH}_2\text{O}_2} \times 100\% = 26.09\%$ C

mass % H = $\dfrac{2.016 \text{ g H}}{46.03 \text{ g CH}_2\text{O}_2} \times 100\% = 4.380\%$ H

mass % O = $\dfrac{32.00 \text{ g O}}{46.03 \text{ g CH}_2\text{O}_2} \times 100\% = 69.52\%$ O

c) mass % C = $\dfrac{36.03 \text{ g C}}{59.11 \text{ g C}_3\text{H}_9\text{N}} \times 100\% = 60.95\%$ C

mass % H = $\dfrac{9.072 \text{ g H}}{59.11 \text{ g C}_3\text{H}_9\text{N}} \times 100\% = 15.35\%$ H

mass % N = $\dfrac{14.01 \text{ g N}}{59.11 \text{ g C}_3\text{H}_9\text{N}} \times 100\% = 23.70\%$ N

d) mass % C = $\dfrac{48.04 \text{ g C}}{88.16 \text{ g C}_4\text{H}_{12}\text{N}_2} \times 100\% = 54.49\%$ C

mass % H = $\dfrac{12.096 \text{ g H}}{88.16 \text{ g C}_4\text{H}_{12}\text{N}_2} \times 100\% = 13.72\%$ H

mass % N = $\dfrac{28.02 \text{ g N}}{88.16 \text{ g C}_4\text{H}_{12}\text{N}_2} \times 100\% = 31.78\%$ N

65. $\text{mass \% Fe} = \dfrac{111.7 \text{ g Fe}}{159.70 \text{ g Fe}_2\text{O}_3} \times 100\% = 69.94\% \text{ Fe}$

$\text{mass \% Fe} = \dfrac{167.55 \text{ g Fe}}{231.55 \text{ g Fe}_3\text{O}_4} \times 100\% = 72.36\% \text{ Fe}$

$\text{mass \% Fe} = \dfrac{55.85 \text{ g Fe}}{115.86 \text{ g FeCO}_3} \times 100\% = 48.20\% \text{ Fe}$

The magnetite ore has the highest iron content.

Calculating Empirical Formulas

67. $1.78 \text{ g N} \times \dfrac{1 \text{ mole N}}{14.01 \text{ g}} = 0.127 \text{ mol N}$

$4.05 \text{ g O} \times \dfrac{1 \text{ mole O}}{16.00 \text{ g}} = 0.253 \text{ mol O}$

$\text{N}_{\frac{0.127}{0.127}}\text{O}_{\frac{0.253}{0.127}} = \text{NO}_2$

69. a) $1.245 \text{ g Ni} \times \dfrac{1 \text{ mole Ni}}{58.69 \text{ g}} = 0.02121 \text{ mol Ni}$

$5.381 \text{ g I} \times \dfrac{1 \text{ mole I}}{126.90 \text{ g}} = 0.04240 \text{ mol I}$

$\text{Ni}_{\frac{0.02121}{0.02121}}\text{I}_{\frac{0.04240}{0.02121}} = \text{NiI}_2$

b) $1.443 \text{ g Se} \times \dfrac{1 \text{ mole Se}}{78.96 \text{ g}} = 0.01828 \text{ mol Se}$

$5.841 \text{ g Br} \times \dfrac{1 \text{ mole Br}}{79.90 \text{ g}} = 0.07310 \text{ mol Br}$

$\text{Se}_{\frac{0.01828}{0.01828}}\text{Br}_{\frac{0.07310}{0.01828}} = \text{SeBr}_4$

69. (cont.)

c) $2.128 \text{ g Be} \times \dfrac{1 \text{ mole Be}}{9.012 \text{ g}} = 0.2361 \text{ mol Be}$

$7.557 \text{ g S} \times \dfrac{1 \text{ mole S}}{32.06 \text{ g}} = 0.2357 \text{ mol S}$

$15.107 \text{ g O} \times \dfrac{1 \text{ mole O}}{16.00 \text{ g}} = 0.9442 \text{ mol O}$

$Be_{\frac{0.2361}{0.2357}} S_{\frac{0.2357}{0.2357}} O_{\frac{0.9442}{0.2357}} = BeSO_4$

71. Assume a 100 gram sample, percentage composition is then equal to the number of grams of each element.

$54.50 \text{ g C} \times \dfrac{1 \text{ mole C}}{12.01 \text{ g}} = 4.538 \text{ mol C}$

$13.73 \text{ g H} \times \dfrac{1 \text{ mole H}}{1.008 \text{ g}} = 13.62 \text{ mol H}$

$31.77 \text{ g N} \times \dfrac{1 \text{ mole N}}{14.01 \text{ g}} = 2.268 \text{ mol N}$

$C_{\frac{4.538}{2.268}} H_{\frac{13.62}{2.268}} N_{\frac{2.268}{2.268}} \Rightarrow C_2H_6N$

73. Assume a 100 gram sample, percentage composition is then equal to the number of grams of each element.

a) $62.04 \text{ g C} \times \dfrac{1 \text{ mole C}}{12.01 \text{ g}} = 5.166 \text{ mole C}$

$10.41 \text{ g H} \times \dfrac{1 \text{ mole g H}}{1.008 \text{ g H}} = 10.33 \text{ moles H}$

$27.55 \text{g O} \times \dfrac{1 \text{ mole g O}}{16.00 \text{ g O}} = 1.722 \text{ moles O}$

$C_{\frac{5.166}{1.722}} H_{\frac{10.33}{1.722}} O_{\frac{1.722}{1.722}} = C_3H_6O$

73. (cont.)

b) $58.80 \text{ g C} \times \dfrac{1 \text{ mole C}}{12.01 \text{ g}} = 4.896 \text{ mole C}$

$9.87 \text{ g H} \times \dfrac{1 \text{ mole g H}}{1.008 \text{ g H}} = 9.792 \text{ moles H}$

$31.33 \text{g O} \times \dfrac{1 \text{ mole g O}}{16.00 \text{ g O}} = 1.958 \text{ moles O}$

$C_{\frac{4.896}{1.958}} H_{\frac{9.792}{1.958}} O_{\frac{1.958}{1.958}} = C_{2.5}H_5O_1$

Empirical Formula $= 2 \times (C_{2.5}H_5O_1) = C_5H_{10}O_2$

c) $71.98 \text{ g C} \times \dfrac{1 \text{ mole C}}{12.01 \text{ g}} = 5.993 \text{ mole C}$

$6.71 \text{ g H} \times \dfrac{1 \text{ mole g H}}{1.008 \text{ g H}} = 6.66 \text{ moles H}$

$21.31 \text{g O} \times \dfrac{1 \text{ mole g O}}{16.00 \text{ g O}} = 1.332 \text{ moles O}$

$C_{\frac{5.993}{1.332}} H_{\frac{6.66}{1.332}} O_{\frac{1.332}{1.332}} = C_{4.50}H_5O_1$

Empirical Formula $= 2 \times (C_{4.50}H_5O_1) = C_9H_{10}O_2$

75. $1.45 \text{ g P} \times \dfrac{1 \text{ mole P}}{30.97 \text{ g P}} = 0.0468 \text{ mole P}$

mass O $= 2.57 - 1.45 = 1.12 \text{ g O}$

$1.12 \text{ g O} \times \dfrac{1 \text{ mole O}}{16.00 \text{ g O}} = 0.0700 \text{ mole O}$

$P_{\frac{0.0468}{0.0468}} O_{\frac{0.0700}{0.0468}} = P_1O_{1.50}$

Empirical Formula $= 2 \times (P_1O_{1.50}) = P_2O_3$

77. $0.77 \text{ mg N} \times \dfrac{1 \text{ g}}{1000 \text{ mg}} \times \dfrac{1 \text{ mole N}}{14.01 \text{ g N}} = 5.50 \times 10^{-5} \text{ mole N}$

mass Cl = 6.61 - 0.77 = 5.84 mg Cl

$5.84 \text{ mg Cl} \times \dfrac{1 \text{ g}}{1000 \text{ mg}} \times \dfrac{1 \text{ mole Cl}}{35.45 \text{ g Cl}} = 1.65 \times 10^{-4} \text{ mole Cl}$

$\text{Ni}_{\frac{5.50 \times 10^{-5}}{5.50 \times 10^{-5}}} \text{Cl}_{\frac{1.65 \times 10^{-4}}{5.50 \times 10^{-5}}} = \text{NCl}_3$

Calculating Molecular Formulas

79. $\dfrac{\text{Molar Mass}}{\text{Empirical Mass}} = \text{Multiplier} \Rightarrow \dfrac{56.11}{14.03} = 4 \Rightarrow 4 \times (\text{CH}_2) = \text{C}_4\text{H}_8$

81. $\dfrac{\text{Molar Mass}}{\text{Empirical Mass}} = \text{Multiplier}$

a) $\dfrac{284.77}{47.46} = 6 \Rightarrow 6 \times (\text{CCl}) = \text{C}_6\text{Cl}_6$

b) $\dfrac{131.39}{131.38} = 1 \Rightarrow 1 \times (\text{C}_2\text{HCl}_3) = \text{C}_2\text{HCl}_3$

c) $\dfrac{181.44}{60.48} = 3 \Rightarrow 3 \times (\text{C}_2\text{HCl}) = \text{C}_6\text{H}_3\text{Cl}_3$

Cumulative Problems

83. $\text{Volume} = \text{L}^3 \Rightarrow (1.42 \text{ cm})^3 = 2.86 \text{ cm}^3$

$\text{mass} = \text{density} \times \text{volume} \Rightarrow (8.96 \text{ g Cu/cm}^3)(2.86 \text{ cm}^3) = 25.6 \text{ g Cu}$

$25.6 \text{ g Cu} \times \dfrac{1 \text{ mole Cu}}{63.55 \text{ g}} \times \dfrac{6.022 \times 10^{23} \text{ Cu atoms}}{1 \text{ mole Cu}} = 2.43 \times 10^{23} \text{ Cu atoms}$

85. Volume: $1 \text{ ml} = 1 \text{ cm}^3 \Rightarrow 0.05 \text{ cm}^3 \text{ H}_2\text{O}$

$\text{mass} = \text{density} \times \text{volume} \Rightarrow (1.0 \text{ g H}_2\text{O/cm}^3)(0.05 \text{ cm}^3) = 0.05 \text{ g H}_2\text{O}$

$0.05 \text{ g H}_2\text{O} \times \dfrac{1 \text{ mole H}_2\text{O}}{18.02 \text{ g}} \times \dfrac{6.022 \times 10^{23} \text{ molecules}}{1 \text{ mole H}_2\text{O}} = 1.67 \times 10^{21} \text{ H}_2\text{O molecules}$

87. a) CuI_2; Formula Mass=317.35

$$\text{Mass \% Cu} = \frac{63.55}{317.35} \times 100\% = 20.03\% \text{ Cu}$$

$$\text{Mass \% I} = \frac{253.8}{317.35} \times 100\% = 79.97\% \text{ I}$$

b) $NaNO_3$; Formula Mass=85.00

$$\text{Mass \% Na} = \frac{22.99}{85.00} \times 100\% = 27.05\%$$

$$\text{Mass \% N} = \frac{14.01}{85.00} \times 100\% = 16.48\%$$

$$\text{Mass \% O} = \frac{48.00}{85.00} \times 100\% = 56.47\% \text{ O}$$

c) $PbSO_4$; Formula Mass=303.3

$$\text{Mass \% Pb} = \frac{207.2}{303.3} \times 100\% = 68.32\% \text{ Pb}$$

$$\text{Mass \% S} = \frac{32.07}{303.3} \times 100\% = 10.57\% \text{ S}$$

$$\text{Mass \% O} = \frac{64.00}{303.3} \times 100\% = 21.10\% \text{ O}$$

d) CaF_2; Formula Mass=78.08

$$\text{Mass \% Ca} = \frac{40.08}{78.08} \times 100\% = 51.33\% \text{ Ca}$$

$$\text{Mass \% F} = \frac{38.00}{78.08} \times 100\% = 48.67\% \text{ F}$$

89. Step 1: Determine how much Fe_2O_3 would be needed to obtain 1×10^3 kg of iron.

$$1.0 \times 10^3 \text{kg Fe} \times \frac{1000 \text{g}}{1 \text{ kg}} \times \frac{1 \text{ mol Fe}}{55.85 \text{ g}} \times \frac{1 \text{ mol Fe}_2\text{O}_3}{2 \text{ mol Fe}} \times \frac{159.70 \text{ g}}{1 \text{ mol Fe}_2\text{O}_3} \times \frac{1 \text{ kg}}{1000 \text{g}} \Rightarrow$$

$$= 1.4 \times 10^3 \text{ kg Fe}_2\text{O}_3$$

89. (cont.)

Step 2: Based on the ore being 78% Fe_2O_3, determine the amount of rock needed for processing. Remember 78% Fe_2O_3 can be used as a conversion factor because 78 kg Fe_2O_3 is obtained for every 100 kg of ore mined.

$$1.4x10^3 \text{ kg } Fe_2O_3 \times \frac{100 \text{ kg rock}}{78 \text{ kg } Fe_2O_3} = 1.8x10^3 \text{ kg rock}$$

91. $\dfrac{12 \text{ kg } CHF_2Cl}{1 \text{ mo}} \times 12 \text{ mo} \times \dfrac{1000 \text{ g}}{1 \text{ kg}} \times \dfrac{1 \text{ mol } CHF_2Cl}{86.47 \text{ g}} \times \dfrac{1 \text{ mol Cl}}{1 \text{ mol } CHF_2Cl} \times \dfrac{35.45 \text{ g}}{1 \text{ mole Cl}} \times$

$$\dfrac{1 \text{ kg}}{1000 \text{ g}} = 59 \text{ kg Cl}$$

93. $1.0 \text{ L } H_2O \times \dfrac{1000 \text{ cm}^3}{1 \text{ L}} \times \dfrac{1 \text{ g } H_2O}{1 \text{ cm}^3} \times \dfrac{1 \text{ mol } H_2O}{18.0 \text{ g}} \times \dfrac{2 \text{ mol H}}{1 \text{ mol } H_2O} \times \dfrac{1.008 \text{ g}}{1 \text{ mol H}}$

$$= 1.1x10^2 \text{ g H}$$

95. Assume a 100 gram sample, % composition then equals the number of grams of each element.

$$55.80 \text{ g C} \times \dfrac{1 \text{ mole C}}{12.01 \text{ g}} = 4.646 \text{ mole C}$$

$$7.03 \text{ g H} \times \dfrac{1 \text{ mole H}}{1.008 \text{ g H}} = 6.974 \text{ moles H}$$

$$37.17 \text{ g O} \times \dfrac{1 \text{ mole O}}{16.00 \text{ g O}} = 2.323 \text{ moles O}$$

$$C_{\frac{4.646}{2.323}} H_{\frac{6.974}{2.323}} O_{\frac{2.323}{2.323}} = C_2H_3O$$

$$\dfrac{\text{Molar Mass}}{\text{Empirical Mass}} = \text{Multiplier} \Rightarrow \dfrac{86.09}{43.04} = 2$$

Molecular Formula $= 2 \times (C_2H_3O) = C_4H_6O_2$

97. Assume a 100 gram sample, % composition then equals the number of grams of each element.

$$74.03 \text{ g C} \times \frac{1 \text{ mole C}}{12.01 \text{ g}} = 6.164 \text{ mole C}$$

$$8.70 \text{ g H} \times \frac{1 \text{ mole H}}{1.008 \text{ g H}} = 8.630 \text{ moles H}$$

$$17.27 \text{ g N} \times \frac{1 \text{ mole N}}{14.01 \text{ g N}} = 1.233 \text{ moles N}$$

$$C_{\frac{6.164}{1.233}} H_{\frac{8.630}{1.233}} N_{\frac{1.233}{1.233}} = C_5 H_7 N$$

$$\frac{\text{Molar Mass}}{\text{Empirical Mass}} = \text{Multiplier} \Rightarrow \frac{162.23}{81.12} = 2$$

Molecular Formula $= 2 \times (C_5 H_7 N) = C_{10} H_{14} N_2$

Highlight Problems

99. a) $V = 4/3 \pi (7 \times 10^8 \text{ m})^3 = 1.4 \times 10^{27} \text{ m}^3$; convert to $\text{cm}^3 \Rightarrow$

$$1.4 \times 10^{27} \text{ m}^3 \times \frac{(100 \text{ cm})^3}{(1 \text{ m})^3} = 1.4 \times 10^{33} \text{ cm}^3;\ \text{calculate grams of H} \Rightarrow$$

$$1.4 \times 10^{33} \text{ cm}^3 \text{ H} \times \frac{1.4 \text{ g H}}{1 \text{ cm}^3} = 2.0 \times 10^{33} \text{ g H};\ \text{convert to moles \& atoms} \Rightarrow$$

$$2.0 \times 10^{33} \text{ g H} \times \frac{1 \text{ mole H}}{1.008 \text{ g}} \times \frac{6.022 \times 10^{23} \text{ atoms}}{1 \text{ mole H}} = 1 \times 10^{57} \text{ H atoms per star}$$

b) $\dfrac{1 \times 10^{57} \text{ H atoms}}{1 \text{ star}} \times \dfrac{1 \times 10^{11} \text{ stars}}{\text{galaxy}} = 1 \times 10^{68}$ H atoms per galaxy

c) $\dfrac{1 \times 10^{68} \text{ H atoms}}{1 \text{ galaxy}} \times \dfrac{1 \times 10^9 \text{ galaxies}}{\text{universe}} = 1 \times 10^{77}$ H atoms in the universe

101. Assume a 100 gram sample, % composition is then equal to number of grams of each element.

$$95.02 \text{ g C} \times \frac{1 \text{ mole C}}{12.01 \text{ g}} = 7.912 \text{ mole C}$$

$$4.98 \text{ g H} \times \frac{1 \text{ mole H}}{1.008 \text{ g H}} = 4.940 \text{ moles H}$$

$$C_{\frac{7.912}{4.940}} H_{\frac{4.940}{4.940}} = C_{1.6}H_1; \text{ Empirical formula} = 5 \times (C_{1.6}H_1) = C_8H_5$$

$$\frac{\text{Molar Mass}}{\text{Empirical Mass}} = \text{Multiplier} \Rightarrow \frac{202.23}{101.12} = 2$$

Molecular Formula $= 2 \times (C_8H_5) = C_{16}H_{10}$

Chemical Reactions

Questions

1. In a reaction, one or more substances change into different substances. Many examples can be given, such as the neutralization of acid with a base (vinegar + baking soda).

3. The following constitute the main evidence that a chemical reaction has occurred:
   1) a color change
   2) formation of a solid
   3) formation of a gas
   4) emission of light
   5) emission of *(or absorption of)* heat

5. a) gas
   b) liquid
   c) solid
   d) aqueous

7.

a)

Element	Reactants	Products
Ag	4	4
O	2	2
C	1	1

Yes, the equation is balanced.

b)

Element	Reactants	Products
Pb	1	1
N	2	2
O	6	6
Na	2	2
Cl	2	2

Yes, the equation is balanced.

c)

Element	Reactants	Products
C	3	3
H	8	8
O	2	10

No, the equation is not balanced.

9. Soluble compounds will dissolve in water, whereas insoluble compounds will not dissolve in water.

11. Polyatomic ions dissolve in water and dissociate into the ions that make up the compound. The polyatomic ion group stays together as one particle. For example, $NaNO_3$ in water will form $Na^+(aq)$ and $NO_3^-(aq)$.

13. The solubility rules are as follows:
    Soluble Compounds
    1. Any compound containing Li^+, Na^+, K^+, or NH_4^+.
    2. Any compound containing NO_3^-, or $C_2H_3O_2^-$.
    3. Most compounds containing Cl^-, Br^-, or I^-.
        Except with Ag^+, Hg_2^{+2}, or Pb^{+2}, they form insoluble compounds.
    4. Most compounds with SO_4^{-2}.
        Except with: Sr^{+2}, Ba^{+2}, Pb^{+2}, or Ca^{+2}, they form insoluble compounds.
    Insoluble Compounds
    a) Most compounds containing OH^- or S^{-2}
        Except with Li^+, Na^+, K^+, or NH_4^+, they form soluble compounds.
        Except when S^{-2} is with Sr^{+2}, Ba^{+2}, or Ca^{+2}, they form soluble compounds.
        Except when OH^- is with Sr^{+2}, Ba^{+2}, or Ca^{+2}, they form slightly soluble compounds.
    b) Most compounds containing CO_3^{-2} or PO_4^{-3}
        Except with Li^+, Na^+, K^+, or NH_4^+, they form soluble compounds.

    These rules are useful because there is no way to predict solubility from looking at the periodic table. These rules allow us to know what compounds will dissolve in water and which ones will not, which is critical when writing chemical equations.

15. The precipitate in a precipitation reaction will always be the insoluble compound. Otherwise, it would dissolve in water, no solid would form and there would be no precipitation reaction.

17. A complete ionic equation shows all soluble ionic compounds as aqueous ions. A net ionic equation only shows those ions that change form from the reactants side to the products side of the equation. An example of each follows:
    Complete Ionic Equation:
    $$Ba^{+2}(aq)+2NO_3^-(aq)+2Na^+(aq)+SO_4^{-2}(aq) \rightarrow BaSO_4(s)+2Na^+(aq)+2NO_3^-(aq)$$
    Net Ionic Equation:
    $$Ba^{+2}(aq) + SO_4^{-2}(aq) \rightarrow BaSO_4(s)$$

19. The properties of acids include a sour taste, the ability to dissolve some metals, and the tendency to form H^+ in solution. The properties of a base are a bitter taste, a slippery feel, and a tendency to form OH^- in solution.

21. A redox reaction occurs when electrons are exchanged between the reactants.
    An example is: $2K(s) + Cl_2(g) \rightarrow 2KCl(s)$

23. You can classify chemical reactions in one of two ways: 1) by the type of chemistry occurring during the reaction, such as acid-base chemistry or precipitation chemistry or 2) by studying what happens to atoms during the reaction. We use both methods for classifying reactions so we can study the similarities and differences between different reactions.

25. Two examples of synthesis reactions:
    b) $2Na(s) + Cl_2(g) \rightarrow 2NaCl(s)$
    c) $CaO(s) + CO_2(g) \rightarrow CaCO_3(s)$

27. Two examples of single-displacement reactions:
    d) $Zn(s) + CuCl_2(aq) \rightarrow ZnCl_2(aq) + Cu(s)$
    e) $Mg(s) + 2HCl(aq) \rightarrow MgCl_2(aq) + H_2(g)$

Problems

Evidence of Chemical Reactions

29. a) A chemical reaction because the initial compounds change to form a solid and a color change occurs.
    b) Not a chemical reaction because the initial compound did not change into another substance.
    c) A chemical reaction because the initial compounds change to form a solid.
    d) A chemical reaction because the initial compounds change to form a gas and other new compounds.

31. Yes, a chemical reaction has occurred because the bubbles that formed are a new compound formed as a product of the reaction.

33. Yes, a chemical reaction has occurred because the color change in the hair is due to forming new compounds in the hair itself.

Writing and Balancing Chemical Equations

35. a) $2Cu(s) + S(s) \rightarrow Cu_2S(s)$

    b) $2SO_2(g) + O_2(g) \rightarrow 2SO_3(g)$

    c) $4HCl(aq) + MnO_2(s) \rightarrow MnCl_2(aq) + 2H_2O(l) + Cl_2(g)$

    d) $2C_6H_6(l) + 15O_2(g) \rightarrow 12CO_2(g) + 6H_2O(l)$

37. a) $Mg(s) + 2CuNO_3(aq) \rightarrow Mg(NO_3)_2(aq) + 2Cu(s)$

    b) $2N_2O_5(g) \rightarrow 4NO_2(g) + O_2(g)$

    c) $Ca(s) + 2HNO_3(aq) \rightarrow Ca(NO_3)_2(aq) + H_2(g)$

    d) $2CH_3OH(l) + 3O_2(g) \rightarrow 2CO_2(g) + 4H_2O(l)$

39. $2Na(s) + 2H_2O(l) \rightarrow H_2(g) + 2NaOH(aq)$

41. $2SO_2(g) + O_2(g) + 2H_2O(l) \rightarrow 2H_2SO_4(aq)$

43. $V_2O_5(s) + 2H_2(g) \rightarrow V_2O_3(s) + 2H_2O(l)$

45. $C_{12}H_{22}O_{11}(aq) + H_2O(l) \rightarrow 4C_2H_5OH(aq) + 4CO_2(g)$

47. a) $3N_2H_4(l) \rightarrow 4NH_3(g) + N_2(g)$

    b) $3H_2(g) + N_2(g) \rightarrow 2NH_3(g)$

    c) $Cu_2O(s) + C(s) \rightarrow 2Cu(s) + CO(g)$

    d) $H_2(g) + Cl_2(g) \rightarrow 2HCl(g)$

49. a) $BaO_2(s) + H_2SO_4(aq) \rightarrow BaSO_4(s) + H_2O_2(aq)$

    b) $2Co(NO_3)_3(aq) + 3(NH_4)_2S(aq) \rightarrow Co_2S_3(s) + 6NH_4NO_3(aq)$

    c) $Li_2O(s) + H_2O(l) \rightarrow 2LiOH(aq)$

    d) $Hg_2(C_2H_3O_2)_2(aq) + 2KCl(aq) \rightarrow Hg_2Cl_2(s) + 2KC_2H_3O_2(aq)$

51. a) incorrect; $4Al(s) + 3O_2(g) \rightarrow 2Al_2O_3(s)$

    b) correct

    c) incorrect; $2NiS(s) + 3O_2(g) \rightarrow 2NiO(s) + 2SO_2(g)$

    d) incorrect; $Fe_2O_3(s) + 3CO(g) \rightarrow 2Fe(s) + 3CO_2(g)$

53. $C_6H_{12}O_6(aq) + 6O_2(g) \rightarrow 6CO_2(g) + 6H_2O(l)$

55. $2NO(g) + 2CO(g) \rightarrow N_2(g) + 2CO_2(g)$

Solubility

57. a) soluble; Na^+, NO_3^-
    b) soluble; Pb^{+2}, $C_2H_3O_2^-$
    c) insoluble
    d) soluble; NH_4^+, S^{-2}

59. Ag^+ with Cl^-, $AgCl$
    Ba^{+2} with SO_4^{-2}, $BaSO_4$
    Cu^{+2} with CO_3^{-2}, $CuCO_3$
    Fe^{+3} with S^{-2}, Fe_2S_3

61. <u>Soluble</u>

    CaS, $LiOH$, K_2S, NH_4Cl, K_2CO_3, *Na_2S*, *SrS*

    <u>Insoluble</u>

    Hg_2Cl_2, $Cu_3(PO_4)_2$, $PbSO_4$, $CaSO_4$, $AgCl$, *Hg_2I_2*, *$PbCl_2$*

    *Those compounds in *italics* have been moved from their original column.

Precipitation Reactions

63. a) $NH_4Cl(aq) + AgNO_3(aq) \rightarrow AgCl(s) + NH_4NO_3(aq)$
    b) NO REACTION
    c) $CrCl_2(aq) + Li_2CO_3(aq) \rightarrow CrCO_3(s) + 2LiCl(aq)$
    d) $3KOH(aq) + FeCl_3(aq) \rightarrow Fe(OH)_3(s) + 3KCl(aq)$

65. a) $Na_2CO_3(aq) + Pb(NO_3)_2(aq) \rightarrow PbCO_3(s) + 2NaNO_3(aq)$
    b) $K_2SO_4(aq) + Pb(C_2H_3O_2)_2(aq) \rightarrow PbSO_4(s) + 2KC_2H_3O_2(aq)$
    c) $Cu(NO_3)_2(aq) + BaS(aq) \rightarrow CuS(s) + Ba(NO_3)_2(aq)$
    d) NO REACTION

67. a) correct
    b) NO REACTION
    c) correct
    d) $Pb(NO_3)_2(aq) + 2 LiCl(aq) \rightarrow 2 LiNO_3(aq) + PbCl_2(s)$

Ionic and Net Ionic Equations

69. Spectator Ions: $C_2H_3O_2^-$, K^+

71. a) Complete Ionic:

$Ag^+(aq) + NO_3^-(aq) + K^+(aq) + Cl^-(aq) \rightarrow AgCl(s) + K^+(aq) + NO_3^-(aq)$

Net Ionic:

$Ag^+(aq) + Cl^-(aq) \rightarrow AgCl(s)$

b) Complete Ionic:

$Ca^{+2}(aq) + S^{-2}(aq) + Cu^{+2}(aq) + 2Cl^-(aq) \rightarrow CuS(s) + Ca^{+2}(aq) + 2Cl^-(aq)$

Net Ionic:

$S^{-2}(aq) + Cu^{+2}(aq) \rightarrow CuS(s)$

c) Complete Ionic:

$Na^+(aq) + OH^-(aq) + H^+(aq) + NO_3^-(aq) \rightarrow H_2O(l) + Na^+(aq) + NO_3^-(aq)$

Net Ionic:

$OH^-(aq) + H^+(aq) \rightarrow H_2O(l)$

d) Complete Ionic:

$6K^+(aq) + 2PO_4^{-3}(aq) + 3Ni^{+2}(aq) + 6Cl^-(aq) \rightarrow Ni_3(PO_4)_2(s) + 6K^+(aq) + 6Cl^-(aq)$

Net Ionic:

$2PO_4^{-3}(aq) + 3Ni^{+2}(aq) \rightarrow Ni_3(PO_4)_2(s)$

73. Complete Ionic:

$Hg_2^{+2}(aq) + 2NO_3^-(aq) + 2Na^+(aq) + 2Cl^-(aq) \rightarrow Hg_2Cl_2(s) + 2Na^+(aq) + 2NO_3^-(aq)$

Net Ionic:

$Hg_2^{+2}(aq) + 2Cl^-(aq) \rightarrow Hg_2Cl_2(s)$

75. a) Complete Ionic:

$2Na^+(aq) + CO_3^{-2}(aq) + Pb^{+2}(aq) + 2NO_3^-(aq) \rightarrow PbCO_3(s) + 2Na^+(aq) + 2NO_3^-(aq)$

Net Ionic:

$CO_3^{-2}(aq) + Pb^{+2}(aq) \rightarrow PbCO_3(s)$

b) Complete Ionic:

$2K^+(aq) + SO_4^{-2}(aq) + Pb^{+2}(aq) + 2C_2H_3O_2^-(aq) \rightarrow PbSO_4(s) + 2K^+(aq) + 2C_2H_3O_2^-(aq)$

Net Ionic:

$SO_4^{-2}(aq) + Pb^{+2}(aq) \rightarrow PbSO_4(s)$

c) Complete Ionic:

$Cu^{+2}(aq) + 2NO_3^-(aq) + Ba^{+2}(aq) + S^{-2}(aq) \rightarrow CuS(s) + Ba^{+2}(aq) + 2NO_3^-(aq)$

Net Ionic:

$Cu^{+2}(aq) + S^{-2}(aq) \rightarrow CuS(s)$

d) NO REACTION

Acid-Base and Gas Evolution Reactions

77. Molecular: $HCl(aq) + KOH(aq) \rightarrow KCl(aq) + H_2O(l)$
    Net Ionic: $H^+(aq) + OH^-(aq) \rightarrow H_2O(l)$

79. a) $2HCl(aq) + Ba(OH)_2(aq) \rightarrow 2H_2O(l) + BaCl_2(aq)$
    b) $H_2SO_4(aq) + 2KOH(aq) \rightarrow 2H_2O(l) + K_2SO_4(aq)$
    c) $HClO_4(aq) + NaOH(aq) \rightarrow H_2O(l) + NaClO_4(aq)$

81. a) $HBr(aq) + NaHCO_3(aq) \rightarrow CO_2(g) + H_2O(l) + NaBr(aq)$
    b) $NH_4I(aq) + KOH(aq) \rightarrow H_2O(l) + NH_3(g) + KI(aq)$
    c) $2HNO_3(aq) + K_2SO_3(aq) \rightarrow SO_2(g) + H_2O(l) + 2KNO_3(aq)$
    d) $2HI(aq) + Li_2S(aq) \rightarrow H_2S(g) + 2LiI(aq)$

Oxidation-Reduction and Combustion

83. b and d

85. a) $2C_2H_6(g) + 7O_2(g) \rightarrow 4CO_2(g) + 6H_2O(g)$
    b) $2Ca(s) + O_2(g) \rightarrow 2CaO(s)$
    c) $2C_3H_8O(l) + 9O_2(g) \rightarrow 6CO_2(g) + 8H_2O(g)$
    d) $2C_4H_{10}S(l) + 15O_2(g) \rightarrow 8CO_2(g) + 10H_2O(g) + 2SO_2(g)$

Classifying Chemical Reactions by What Atoms Do

87. a) decomposition
    b) synthesis
    c) displacement
    d) double displacement

89. a) double displacement
    b) synthesis
    c) synthesis

Cumulative Problems

91. a) Complete Ionic:
        $2Na^+(aq) + 2I^-(aq) + Hg_2^{+2}(aq) + 2NO_3^-(aq) \rightarrow Hg_2I_2(s) + 2Na^+(aq) + 2NO_3^-(aq)$
    Net Ionic:
        $2I^-(aq) + Hg_2^{+2}(aq) \rightarrow Hg_2I_2(s)$
    b) Complete Ionic:
        $2H^+(aq) + 2ClO_4^-(aq) + Ba^{+2}(aq) + 2OH^-(aq) \rightarrow 2H_2O(l) + 2ClO_4^-(aq) + Ba^{+2}(aq)$
    Net Ionic:
        $H^+(aq) + OH^-(aq) \rightarrow H_2O(l)$
    c) NO REACTION
    d) Complete Ionic:
        $2H^+(aq) + 2Cl^-(aq) + 2Li^+(aq) + CO_3^{-2}(aq) \rightarrow CO_2(g) + H_2O(l) + 2Li^+(aq) + 2Cl^-(aq)$
    Net Ionic:
        $2H^+(aq) + CO_3^{-2}(aq) \rightarrow CO_2(g) + H_2O(l)$

93. a) NO REACTION
  b) NO REACTION
  c) Complete Ionic:
       $H^+(aq) + NO_3^-(aq) + K^+(aq) + HSO_3^-(aq) \rightarrow SO_2(g) + H_2O(l) + NO_3^-(aq) + K^+(aq)$
       Net Ionic: $\quad H^+(aq) + HSO_3^-(aq) \rightarrow SO_2(g) + H_2O(l)$
  d) Complete Ionic:
       $Mn^{+3}(aq) + 3Cl^-(aq) + 3K^+(aq) + PO_4^{-3}(aq) \rightarrow MnPO_4(s) + 3Cl^-(aq) + 3K^+(aq)$
       Net Ionic:
       $Mn^{+3}(aq) + PO_4^{-3}(aq) \rightarrow MnPO_4(s)$

95. a) acid-base; $KOH(aq) + HC_2H_3O_2(aq) \rightarrow H_2O(l) + KC_2H_3O_2(aq)$
  b) gas-evolution/acid-base: $2HBr(aq) + K_2CO_3(aq) \rightarrow H_2O(l) + CO_2(g) + 2KBr(aq)$
  c) synthesis: $2H_2(g) + O_2(g) \rightarrow 2H_2O(g)$
  d) precipitation: $2NH_4Cl(aq) + Pb(NO_3)_2(aq) \rightarrow PbCl_2(s) + 2NH_4NO_3(aq)$

97. For calcium chloride:
      Molecular: $3CaCl_2(aq) + 2Na_3PO_4(aq) \rightarrow Ca_3(PO_4)_2(s) + 6NaCl(aq)$
      Complete: $3Ca^{+2}(aq) + 6Cl^-(aq) + 6Na^+(aq) + 2PO_4^{-3}(aq) \rightarrow$
              $Ca_3(PO_4)_2(s) + 6Na^+(aq) + 6Cl^-(aq)$
      Net Ionic: $3Ca^{+2}(aq) + 2PO_4^{-3}(aq) \rightarrow Ca_3(PO_4)_2(s)$
      For magnesium nitrate:
      Molecular: $3Mg(NO_3)_2(aq) + 2Na_3PO_4(aq) \rightarrow Mg_3(PO_4)_2(s) + 6NaNO_3(aq)$
      Complete: $3Mg^{+2}(aq) + 6NO_3^-(aq) + 6Na^+(aq) + 2PO_4^{-3}(aq) \rightarrow$
              $Mg_3(PO_4)_2(s) + 6Na^+(aq) + 6NO_3^-(aq)$
      Net Ionic: $3Mg^{+2}(aq) + 2PO_4^{-3}(aq) \rightarrow Mg_3(PO_4)_2(s)$

99. 1) The silver ion is not present as it would precipitate with chloride ions.
   2) Sulfate will only precipitate the calcium ion, not the copper(II) ion:
      $Ca^{+2}(aq) + SO_4^{-2}(aq) \rightarrow CaSO_4(s)$
   3) The only possible ion left is copper(II), which will precipitate with carbonate:
      $Cu^{+2}(aq) + CO_3^{-2}(aq) \rightarrow CuCO_3(s)$
   Therefore, the calcium and copper(II) ions were present in the original solution.

Highlight Problems

101. Figure 7.9 is the air bag based on a chemical reaction. You can see the changes
    in the arrangement of atoms within the compounds before and after detonation.

Quantities in Chemical Reactions 8

Questions

1. The reaction stoichiometry is important because it allows us to calculate how much reactants should be used to form a desired amount of a product. It can be thought of as a recipe for a desired compound. Just think, if we had no way to determine the amount of raw ingredients needed to make a drug in the pharmaceutical industry, there would be no way to produce sufficient amounts at a reasonable cost.

3. 1 mole $N_2(g)$ ≡ 3 moles $H_2(g)$ ≡ 2 moles $NH_3(g)$

5. $\dfrac{2 \text{ moles NaCl}}{1 \text{ mole Cl}_2}$

7. mass reactant → moles reactant → moles product → mass product

9. The limiting reactant is the reactant that determines the maximum amount of product that can be produced in a reaction.

11. Because most chemical reactions do not actually make 100% of the theoretical yield, we usually have less produced. This is called the actual yield. The percent yield is the percent of the theoretical yield that was actually made.

13. d) because we would have many more moles of B than A under these conditions.

Problems

Mole-to-Mole Conversions

15. a) $1 \text{ mol A} \times \dfrac{1 \text{ mol C}}{1 \text{ mol A}} = 1 \text{ mol C}$

b) $1 \text{ mol B} \times \dfrac{1 \text{ mol C}}{2 \text{ mol B}} = 0.5 \text{ mol C}$

c) $2 \text{ mol A} \times \dfrac{1 \text{ mol C}}{1 \text{ mol A}} = 2 \text{ mol C}$

d) $2 \text{ mol B} \times \dfrac{1 \text{ mol C}}{2 \text{ mol B}} = 1 \text{ mol C}$

17. a) $1.3 \text{ mol N}_2\text{O}_5 \times \dfrac{4 \text{ mol NO}_2}{2 \text{ mol N}_2\text{O}_5} = 2.6 \text{ mol NO}_2$

b) $5.8 \text{ mol N}_2\text{O}_5 \times \dfrac{4 \text{ mol NO}_2}{2 \text{ mol N}_2\text{O}_5} = 11.6 \text{ mol NO}_2$

c) $4.45 \times 10^3 \text{ mol N}_2\text{O}_5 \times \dfrac{4 \text{ mol NO}_2}{2 \text{ mol N}_2\text{O}_5} = 8.90 \times 10^3 \text{ mol NO}_2$

d) $1.006 \times 10^{-3} \text{ mol N}_2\text{O}_5 \times \dfrac{4 \text{ mol NO}_2}{2 \text{ mol N}_2\text{O}_5} = 2.012 \times 10^{-3} \text{ mol NO}_2$

19. a) $1.48 \text{ mol H}_2 \times \dfrac{2 \text{ mol HCl}}{1 \text{ mol H}_2} = 2.96 \text{ mol HCl}$

b) $1.48 \text{ mol O}_2 \times \dfrac{2 \text{ mol H}_2\text{O}}{1 \text{ mol O}_2} = 2.96 \text{ mol H}_2\text{O}$

c) $1.48 \text{ mol Na} \times \dfrac{1 \text{ mol Na}_2\text{O}_2}{2 \text{ mol Na}} = 0.740 \text{ mol HCl}$

d) $1.48 \text{ mol O}_2 \times \dfrac{2 \text{ mol SO}_3}{3 \text{ mol O}_2} = 0.987 \text{ mol HCl}$

21. a) $1.2 \text{ mol PbS} \times \dfrac{2 \text{ mol PbO}}{2 \text{ mol PbS}} = 1.2 \text{ mol PbO}$

$1.2 \text{ mol PbS} \times \dfrac{2 \text{ mol SO}_2}{2 \text{ mol PbS}} = 1.2 \text{ mol SO}_2$

b) $1.2 \text{ mol O}_2 \times \dfrac{2 \text{ mol PbO}}{3 \text{ mol O}_2} = 0.80 \text{ mol PbS}$

$1.2 \text{ mol O}_2 \times \dfrac{2 \text{ mol SO}_2}{3 \text{ mol O}_2} = 0.80 \text{ mol SO}_2$

c) $7.9 \text{ mol PbS} \times \dfrac{2 \text{ mol PbO}}{2 \text{ mol PbS}} = 7.9 \text{ mol PbO}$

$7.9 \text{ mol PbS} \times \dfrac{2 \text{ mol SO}_2}{2 \text{ mol PbS}} = 7.9 \text{ mol SO}_2$

21. (cont.)

d) $7.9 \text{ mol } O_2 \times \dfrac{2 \text{ mol PbO}}{3 \text{ mol } O_2} = 5.3 \text{ mol PbS}$

$7.9 \text{ mol } O_2 \times \dfrac{2 \text{ mol } SO_2}{3 \text{ mol } O_2} = 5.3 \text{ mol } SO_2$

23.

mol N_2H_4	mol N_2O_4	mol N_2	mol H_2O
4	2	6	8
6	3	9	12
3	1.5	4.5	6
5.8	2.9	8.7	11.6
13.4	6.7	20.1	26.8
15	7.5	22.5	30

25. $2C_4H_{10}(g) + 13O_2(g) \rightarrow 8CO_2(g) + 10 H_2O(g)$

$4.9 \text{ mol } C_4H_{10} \times \dfrac{13 \text{ mol } O_2}{2 \text{ mol } C_4H_{10}} = 32 \text{ mol } O_2$

27. a) $Pb(s) + 2AgNO_3(aq) \rightarrow Pb(NO_3)_2(aq) + 2Ag(s)$

b) $9.3 \text{ mol Pb} \times \dfrac{2 \text{ mol } AgNO_3}{1 \text{ mol Pb}} = 19 \text{ mol } AgNO_3$

c) $28.4 \text{ mol Pb} \times \dfrac{2 \text{ mol Ag}}{1 \text{ mol Pb}} = 56.8 \text{ mol Ag}$

Mass-to-Mass Conversions

29. a) $2.88 \text{ g HgO} \times \dfrac{1 \text{ mol HgO}}{216.59 \text{ g}} \times \dfrac{1 \text{ mol } O_2}{2 \text{ mol HgO}} \times \dfrac{32.00 \text{ g}}{1 \text{ mol } O_2} = 0.213 \text{ g } O_2$

b) $5.21 \text{ g HgO} \times \dfrac{1 \text{ mol HgO}}{216.59 \text{ g}} \times \dfrac{1 \text{ mol } O_2}{2 \text{ mol HgO}} \times \dfrac{32.00 \text{ g}}{1 \text{ mol } O_2} = 0.385 \text{ g } O_2$

29. (cont.)

c) $1.3x10^3 \text{ g HgO} \times \dfrac{1 \text{ mol HgO}}{216.59 \text{ g}} \times \dfrac{1 \text{ mol O}_2}{2 \text{ mol HgO}} \times \dfrac{32.00 \text{ g}}{1 \text{ mol O}_2} = 96 \text{ g O}_2$

d) $4.6x10^{-3} \text{ g HgO} \times \dfrac{1 \text{ mol HgO}}{216.59 \text{ g}} \times \dfrac{1 \text{ mol O}_2}{2 \text{ mol HgO}} \times \dfrac{32.00 \text{ g}}{1 \text{ mol O}_2} = 3.4x10^{-4} \text{ g O}_2$

31. a) $1.8 \text{ g Cl}_2 \times \dfrac{1 \text{ mol Cl}_2}{70.90 \text{ g}} \times \dfrac{2 \text{ mol NaCl}}{1 \text{ mol Cl}_2} \times \dfrac{58.44 \text{ g}}{1 \text{ mol NaCl}} = 3.0 \text{ g NaCl}$

b) $1.8 \text{ g CaO} \times \dfrac{1 \text{ mol CaO}}{56.08 \text{ g}} \times \dfrac{1 \text{ mol CaCO}_3}{1 \text{ mol CaO}} \times \dfrac{100.09 \text{ g}}{1 \text{ mol CaCO}_3} = 3.2 \text{ g CaCO}_3$

c) $1.8 \text{ g Mg} \times \dfrac{1 \text{ mol Mg}}{24.31 \text{ g}} \times \dfrac{2 \text{ mol MgO}}{2 \text{ mol Mg}} \times \dfrac{40.31 \text{ g}}{1 \text{ mol MgO}} = 3.0 \text{ g MgO}$

d) $1.8 \text{ g Na}_2\text{O} \times \dfrac{1 \text{ mol Na}_2\text{O}}{61.98 \text{ g}} \times \dfrac{2 \text{ mol NaOH}}{1 \text{ mol Na}_2\text{O}} \times \dfrac{40.00 \text{ g}}{1 \text{ mol NaOH}} = 2.3 \text{ g NaOH}$

33. a) $4.7 \text{ g Al} \times \dfrac{1 \text{ mol Al}}{26.98 \text{ g}} \times \dfrac{1 \text{ mol Al}_2\text{O}_3}{2 \text{ mol Al}} \times \dfrac{101.96 \text{ g}}{1 \text{ mol Al}_2\text{O}_3} = 8.9 \text{ g Al}_2\text{O}_3$

$4.7 \text{ g Al} \times \dfrac{1 \text{ mol Al}}{26.98 \text{ g}} \times \dfrac{2 \text{ mol Fe}}{2 \text{ mol Al}} \times \dfrac{55.85 \text{ g}}{1 \text{ mol Fe}} = 9.7 \text{ g Fe}$

b) $4.7 \text{ g Fe}_2\text{O}_3 \times \dfrac{1 \text{ mol Fe}_2\text{O}_3}{159.70 \text{ g}} \times \dfrac{1 \text{ mol Al}_2\text{O}_3}{1 \text{ mol Fe}_2\text{O}_3} \times \dfrac{101.96 \text{ g}}{1 \text{ mol Al}_2\text{O}_3} = 3.0 \text{ g Al}_2\text{O}_3$

$4.7 \text{ g Fe}_2\text{O}_3 \times \dfrac{1 \text{ mol Fe}_2\text{O}_3}{159.70 \text{ g}} \times \dfrac{2 \text{ mol Fe}}{1 \text{ mol Fe}_2\text{O}_3} \times \dfrac{55.85 \text{ g}}{1 \text{ mol Fe}} = 3.3 \text{ g Fe}$

35. a) $2.5 \text{ g NaOH} \times \dfrac{1 \text{ mol NaOH}}{40.00 \text{ g}} \times \dfrac{1 \text{ mol HCl}}{1 \text{ mol NaOH}} \times \dfrac{36.46 \text{ g}}{1 \text{ mol HCl}} = 2.3 \text{ g HCl}$

b) $2.5 \text{ g Ca(OH)}_2 \times \dfrac{1 \text{ mol Ca(OH)}_2}{74.10 \text{ g}} \times \dfrac{2 \text{ mol HNO}_3}{1 \text{ mol Ca(OH)}_2} \times \dfrac{63.02 \text{ g}}{1 \text{ mol HNO}_3}$

$= 4.3 \text{ g HNO}_3$

c) $2.5 \text{ g KOH} \times \dfrac{1 \text{ mol KOH}}{56.11 \text{ g}} \times \dfrac{1 \text{ mol H}_2\text{SO}_4}{2 \text{ mol KOH}} \times \dfrac{98.09 \text{ g}}{1 \text{ mol H}_2\text{SO}_4} = 2.2 \text{ g H}_2\text{SO}_4$

37. $22.5 \text{ g Al} \times \dfrac{1 \text{ mol Al}}{26.98 \text{ g}} \times \dfrac{3 \text{ mol H}_2\text{SO}_4}{2 \text{ mol Al}} \times \dfrac{98.09 \text{ g}}{1 \text{ mol H}_2\text{SO}_4} = 123 \text{ g H}_2\text{SO}_4$

$22.5 \text{ g Al} \times \dfrac{1 \text{ mol Al}}{26.98 \text{ g}} \times \dfrac{3 \text{ mol H}_2}{2 \text{ mol Al}} \times \dfrac{2.016 \text{ g}}{1 \text{ mol H}_2} = 2.52 \text{ g H}_2$

Limiting Reactant, Theoretical Yield, and Percent Yield

39. a) $2 \text{ mol A} \times \dfrac{3 \text{ mol C}}{2 \text{ mol A}} = 3 \text{ mol C}$

$5 \text{ mol B} \times \dfrac{3 \text{ mol C}}{4 \text{ mol B}} = 3.75 \text{ mol C}$ ∴ The limiting reactant is A.

b) $1.8 \text{ mol A} \times \dfrac{3 \text{ mol C}}{2 \text{ mol A}} = 2.7 \text{ mol C}$

$4 \text{ mol B} \times \dfrac{3 \text{ mol C}}{4 \text{ mol B}} = 3 \text{ mol C}$ ∴ The limiting reactant is A.

c) $3 \text{ mol A} \times \dfrac{3 \text{ mol C}}{2 \text{ mol A}} = 4.5 \text{ mol C}$

$4 \text{ mol B} \times \dfrac{3 \text{ mol C}}{4 \text{ mol B}} = 3 \text{ mol C}$ ∴ The limiting reactant is B.

d) $22 \text{ mol A} \times \dfrac{3 \text{ mol C}}{2 \text{ mol A}} = 33 \text{ mol C}$

$40 \text{ mol B} \times \dfrac{3 \text{ mol C}}{4 \text{ mol B}} = 30 \text{ mol C}$ ∴ The limiting reactant is B.

41. a) $1 \text{ mol A} \times \dfrac{3 \text{ mol C}}{1 \text{ mol A}} = 3 \text{ mol C}$

$1 \text{ mol B} \times \dfrac{3 \text{ mol C}}{2 \text{ mol B}} = 1.5 \text{ mol C}$

The limiting reactant is B. Therefore, the theoretical yield of C is 1.5 mol.

b) $2 \text{ mol A} \times \dfrac{3 \text{ mol C}}{1 \text{ mol A}} = 6 \text{ mol C}$

$2 \text{ mol B} \times \dfrac{3 \text{ mol C}}{2 \text{ mol B}} = 3 \text{ mol C}$

The limiting reactant is B. Therefore, the theoretical yield of C is 3 mol.

41. (cont.)

c) $1 \text{ mol A} \times \dfrac{3 \text{ mol C}}{1 \text{ mol A}} = 3 \text{ mol C}$

$3 \text{ mol B} \times \dfrac{3 \text{ mol C}}{2 \text{ mol B}} = 4.5 \text{ mol C}$

The limiting reactant is A. Therefore, the theoretical yield of C is 3 mol.

d) $32 \text{ mol A} \times \dfrac{3 \text{ mol C}}{1 \text{ mol A}} = 96 \text{ mol C}$

$68 \text{ mol B} \times \dfrac{3 \text{ mol C}}{2 \text{ mol B}} = 102 \text{ mol C}$

The limiting reactant is A. Therefore, the theoretical yield of C is 96 mol.

43. a) $1 \text{ mol K} \times \dfrac{2 \text{ mol KCl}}{2 \text{ mol K}} = 1 \text{ mol KCl}$

$1 \text{ mol Cl}_2 \times \dfrac{2 \text{ mol KCl}}{1 \text{ mol Cl}_2} = 2 \text{ mol KCl} \quad \therefore \quad$ The limiting reactant is K.

b) $1.8 \text{ mol K} \times \dfrac{2 \text{ mol KCl}}{2 \text{ mol K}} = 1.8 \text{ mol KCl}$

$1 \text{ mol Cl}_2 \times \dfrac{2 \text{ mol KCl}}{1 \text{ mol Cl}_2} = 2 \text{ mol KCl} \quad \therefore \quad$ The limiting reactant is K.

c) $2.2 \text{ mol K} \times \dfrac{2 \text{ mol KCl}}{2 \text{ mol K}} = 2.2 \text{ mol KCl}$

$1 \text{ mol Cl}_2 \times \dfrac{2 \text{ mol KCl}}{1 \text{ mol Cl}_2} = 2 \text{ mol KCl} \quad \therefore \quad$ The limiting reactant is Cl_2.

d) $14.6 \text{ mol K} \times \dfrac{2 \text{ mol KCl}}{2 \text{ mol K}} = 14.6 \text{ mol KCl}$

$7.8 \text{ mol Cl}_2 \times \dfrac{2 \text{ mol KCl}}{1 \text{ mol Cl}_2} = 15.6 \text{ mol KCl} \quad \therefore \quad$ The limiting reactant is K.

45. a) $2 \text{ mol Mn} \times \dfrac{2 \text{ mol MnO}_3}{2 \text{ mol Mn}} = 2 \text{ mol MnO}_3$

$2 \text{ mol O}_2 \times \dfrac{2 \text{ mol MnO}_3}{3 \text{ mol O}_2} = 1.3 \text{ mol MnO}_3$

The limiting reactant is O_2, $\therefore$ the theoretical yield of MnO_3 is 1.3 mol.

b) $4.8 \text{ mol Mn} \times \dfrac{2 \text{ mol MnO}_3}{2 \text{ mol Mn}} = 4.8 \text{ mol MnO}_3$

$8.5 \text{ mol O}_2 \times \dfrac{2 \text{ mol MnO}_3}{3 \text{ mol O}_2} = 5.7 \text{ mol MnO}_3$

The limiting reactant is Mn, $\therefore$ the theoretical yield of MnO_3 is 4.8 mol.

c) $0.114 \text{ mol Mn} \times \dfrac{2 \text{ mol MnO}_3}{2 \text{ mol Mn}} = 0.114 \text{ mol MnO}_3$

$0.161 \text{ mol O}_2 \times \dfrac{2 \text{ mol MnO}_3}{3 \text{ mol O}_2} = 0.107 \text{ mol MnO}_3$

The limiting reactant is Mn, $\therefore$ the theoretical yield of MnO_3 is 0.107 mol.

d) $27.5 \text{ mol Mn} \times \dfrac{2 \text{ mol MnO}_3}{2 \text{ mol Mn}} = 27.5 \text{ mol MnO}_3$

$43.8 \text{ mol O}_2 \times \dfrac{2 \text{ mol MnO}_3}{3 \text{ mol O}_2} = 29.2 \text{ mol MnO}_3$

The limiting reactant is Mn, $\therefore$ the theoretical yield of MnO_3 is 27.5 mol.

47. a) $1.0 \text{ g Li} \times \dfrac{1 \text{ mol Li}}{6.941 \text{ g}} \times \dfrac{2 \text{ mol LiF}}{2 \text{ mol Li}} = 0.14 \text{ mol LiF}$

$1.0 \text{ g F}_2 \times \dfrac{1 \text{ mol F}_2}{38.00 \text{ g}} \times \dfrac{2 \text{ mol LiF}}{1 \text{ mol F}_2} = 0.053 \text{ mol LiF} \therefore \text{Limiting reactant is } F_2.$

b) $10.5 \text{ g Li} \times \dfrac{1 \text{ mol Li}}{6.941 \text{ g}} \times \dfrac{2 \text{ mol LiF}}{2 \text{ mol Li}} = 1.51 \text{ mol LiF}$

$37.2 \text{ g F}_2 \times \dfrac{1 \text{ mol F}_2}{38.00 \text{ g}} \times \dfrac{2 \text{ mol LiF}}{1 \text{ mol F}_2} = 1.96 \text{ mol LiF} \therefore \text{Limiting reactant is Li.}$

47. (cont.)

c) $2.85 \times 10^3 \text{ g Li} \times \dfrac{1 \text{ mol Li}}{6.941 \text{ g}} \times \dfrac{2 \text{ mol LiF}}{2 \text{ mol Li}} = 411 \text{ mol LiF}$

$6.79 \times 10^3 \text{ g F}_2 \times \dfrac{1 \text{ mol F}_2}{38.00 \text{ g}} \times \dfrac{2 \text{ mol LiF}}{1 \text{ mol F}_2} = 357 \text{ mol LiF} \therefore$ Limiting reactant is F_2.

49. a) $1.0 \text{ g Al} \times \dfrac{1 \text{ mol Al}}{26.98 \text{ g}} \times \dfrac{2 \text{ mol AlCl}_3}{2 \text{ mol Al}} \times \dfrac{133.33 \text{ g}}{1 \text{ mol AlCl}_3} = 4.9 \text{ g AlCl}_3$

$1.0 \text{ g Cl}_2 \times \dfrac{1 \text{ mol Cl}_2}{70.90 \text{ g}} \times \dfrac{2 \text{ mol AlCl}_3}{3 \text{ mol Cl}_2} \times \dfrac{133.33 \text{ g}}{1 \text{ mol AlCl}_3} = 1.3 \text{ g AlCl}_3$

The limiting reactant is Cl_2, $\therefore$ the theoretical yield is 1.3 g of $AlCl_3$.

b) $5.5 \text{ g Al} \times \dfrac{1 \text{ mol Al}}{26.98 \text{ g}} \times \dfrac{2 \text{ mol AlCl}_3}{2 \text{ mol Al}} \times \dfrac{133.33 \text{ g}}{1 \text{ mol AlCl}_3} = 27 \text{ g AlCl}_3$

$19.8 \text{ g Cl}_2 \times \dfrac{1 \text{ mol Cl}_2}{70.90 \text{ g}} \times \dfrac{2 \text{ mol AlCl}_3}{3 \text{ mol Cl}_2} \times \dfrac{133.33 \text{ g}}{1 \text{ mol AlCl}_3} = 24.8 \text{ g AlCl}_3$

The limiting reactant is Cl_2, $\therefore$ the theoretical yield is 24.8 g of $AlCl_3$.

c) $0.439 \text{ g Al} \times \dfrac{1 \text{ mol Al}}{26.98 \text{ g}} \times \dfrac{2 \text{ mol AlCl}_3}{2 \text{ mol Al}} \times \dfrac{133.33 \text{ g}}{1 \text{ mol AlCl}_3} = 2.17 \text{ g AlCl}_3$

$2.29 \text{ g Cl}_2 \times \dfrac{1 \text{ mol Cl}_2}{70.90 \text{ g}} \times \dfrac{2 \text{ mol AlCl}_3}{3 \text{ mol Cl}_2} \times \dfrac{133.33 \text{ g}}{1 \text{ mol AlCl}_3} = 2.87 \text{ g AlCl}_3$

The limiting reactant is Al, $\therefore$ the theoretical yield is 2.17 g $AlCl_3$.

51. $\% \text{ Yield} = \dfrac{18.5}{24.8} \times 100\% = 74.6\%$

53. $14.4 \text{ g CaO} \times \dfrac{1 \text{ mol CaO}}{56.08 \text{ g}} \times \dfrac{1 \text{ mol CaCO}_3}{1 \text{ mol CaO}} \times \dfrac{100.09 \text{ g}}{1 \text{ mol CaCO}_3} = 25.7 \text{ g CaCO}_3$

$13.8 \text{ g CO}_2 \times \dfrac{1 \text{ mol CO}_2}{44.01 \text{ g}} \times \dfrac{1 \text{ mol CaCO}_3}{1 \text{ mol CO}_2} \times \dfrac{100.09 \text{ g}}{1 \text{ mol CaCO}_3} = 31.4 \text{ g CaCO}_3$

The limiting reactant is CaO.

The theoretical yield is 25.7 g $CaCO_3$.

The % Yield $= \dfrac{19.4}{25.7} \times 100\% = 75.5\%$

55. $11.2 \text{ g NiS}_2 \times \dfrac{1 \text{ mol NiS}_2}{122.83 \text{ g}} \times \dfrac{2 \text{ mol NiO}}{2 \text{ mol NiS}_2} \times \dfrac{74.69 \text{ g}}{1 \text{ mol NiO}} = 6.81 \text{ g NiO}$

$5.43 \text{ g O}_2 \times \dfrac{1 \text{ mol O}_2}{32.00 \text{ g}} \times \dfrac{2 \text{ mol NiO}}{5 \text{ mol O}_2} \times \dfrac{74.69 \text{ g}}{1 \text{ mol NiO}} = 5.07 \text{ g NiO}$

The limiting reactant is O_2.

The theoretical yield is 5.07 g NiO.

The % Yield $= \dfrac{4.86}{5.07} \times 100\% = 95.9\%$

57. $135.8 \text{ g NaCl} \times \dfrac{1 \text{ mol NaCl}}{58.44 \text{ g}} \times \dfrac{1 \text{ mol PbCl}_2}{2 \text{ mol NaCl}} \times \dfrac{278.1 \text{ g}}{1 \text{ mol PbCl}_2} = 323.1 \text{ g PbCl}_2$

$195.7 \text{ g Pb}^{+2} \times \dfrac{1 \text{ mol Pb}^{+2}}{207.2 \text{ g}} \times \dfrac{1 \text{ mol PbCl}_2}{1 \text{ mol Pb}^{+2}} \times \dfrac{278.1 \text{ g}}{1 \text{ mol PbCl}_2} = 262.7 \text{ g PbCl}_2$

The limiting reactant is Pb^{+2}.

The theoretical yield is 262.7 g $PbCl_2$.

The % Yield $= \dfrac{252.4}{262.7} \times 100\% = 96.1\%$

Cumulative Problems

59. $NaHCO_3(aq) + HCl(aq) \rightarrow H_2O(l) + CO_2(g) + NaCl(aq)$

$3.5 \text{ g NaHCO}_3 \times \dfrac{1 \text{ mol NaHCO}_3}{84.01 \text{ g}} \times \dfrac{1 \text{ mol HCl}}{1 \text{ mol NaHCO}_3} \times \dfrac{36.46 \text{ g}}{1 \text{ mol HCl}} = 1.5 \text{ g HCl}$

61. $2C_8H_{18}(l) + 25O_2(g) \rightarrow 18H_2O(l) + 16CO_2(g)$

$$1.0 \text{kg } C_8H_{18} \times \frac{1 \times 10^3 \text{g}}{1 \text{kg}} \times \frac{1 \text{ mol } C_8H_{18}}{114.22 \text{ g}} \times \frac{16 \text{ mol } CO_2}{2 \text{ mol } C_8H_{18}} \times \frac{44.01 \text{ g}}{1 \text{ mol } CO_2} \times \frac{1 \text{ kg}}{1 \times 10^3 \text{g}}$$

$= 3.0 \text{ kg } CO_2$

63. $3CaCl_2(aq) + 2Na_3PO_4(aq) \rightarrow Ca_3(PO_4)_2(s) + 6NaCl(aq)$

$$4.8 \text{ g } CaCl_2 \times \frac{1 \text{ mol } CaCl_2}{110.98 \text{ g}} \times \frac{2 \text{ mol } Na_3PO_4}{3 \text{ mol } CaCl_2} \times \frac{163.94 \text{ g}}{1 \text{ mol } Na_3PO_4} = 4.7 \text{ g } Na_3PO_4$$

65. $Zn(s) + 2HCl(aq) \rightarrow H_2(g) + ZnCl_2(aq)$

$$14.5 \text{ g } H_2 \times \frac{1 \text{ mol } H_2}{2.016 \text{ g}} \times \frac{1 \text{ mol } Zn}{1 \text{ mol } H_2} \times \frac{65.39 \text{ g}}{1 \text{ mol } Zn} = 4.70 \times 10^2 \text{ g } Zn$$

67. $$5.00 \text{ mL } C_4H_6O_3 \times \frac{1.08 \text{g}}{1 \text{ mL}} \times \frac{1 \text{ mol } C_4H_6O_3}{102.09 \text{ g}} \times \frac{1 \text{ mol } C_9H_8O_4}{1 \text{ mol } C_4H_6O_3} \times \frac{180.15 \text{ g}}{1 \text{ mol } C_9H_8O_4}$$

$= 9.53 \text{ g } C_9H_8O_4$

$$2.08 \text{ g } C_7H_6O_3 \times \frac{1 \text{ mol } C_7H_6O_3}{138.12 \text{ g}} \times \frac{1 \text{ mol } C_9H_8O_4}{1 \text{ mol } C_7H_6O_3} \times \frac{180.15 \text{ g}}{1 \text{ mol } C_9H_8O_4}$$

$= 2.71 \text{ g } C_9H_8O_4$

The limiting reagent is salicylic acid, $C_7H_6O_3$.

The theoretical yield of aspirin, $C_9H_8O_4$, is then 2.71 g.

The % Yield $= \dfrac{2.08}{2.71} \times 100\% = 76.8\%$

69. $68.2 \text{ kg NH}_3 \times \dfrac{1 \times 10^3 \text{ g}}{1 \text{ kg}} \times \dfrac{1 \text{ mol NH}_3}{17.04 \text{ g}} \times \dfrac{1 \text{ mol CH}_4\text{N}_2\text{O}}{2 \text{ mol NH}_3} \times \dfrac{60.07 \text{ g}}{1 \text{ mol CH}_4\text{N}_2\text{O}} \times \dfrac{1 \text{ kg}}{1000 \text{ g}}$

$=1.20 \times 10^2 \text{ kg CH}_4\text{N}_2\text{O}$

$105 \text{ kg CO}_2 \times \dfrac{1 \times 10^3 \text{ g}}{1 \text{ kg}} \times \dfrac{1 \text{ mol CO}_2}{44.01 \text{ g}} \times \dfrac{1 \text{ mol CH}_4\text{N}_2\text{O}}{1 \text{ mol CO}_2} \times \dfrac{60.06 \text{ g}}{1 \text{ mol CH}_4\text{N}_2\text{O}} \times \dfrac{1 \text{ kg}}{1000 \text{ g}}$

$=143 \text{ kg CH}_4\text{N}_2\text{O}$

The limiting reagent is ammonia, NH_3.

The theoretical yield of urea is then 118 kg.

The % Yield $= \dfrac{87.5}{120} \times 100\% = 72.9\%$

Highlight Problems

71. The balloon in (b) has a 2:1 ratio of reactants that matches the reaction stoichiometry.

73. $2C_8H_{18}(l) + 25O_2(g) \rightarrow 18H_2O(l) + 16CO_2(g)$

$7 \times 10^{12} \text{kg C}_8\text{H}_{18} \times \dfrac{1 \times 10^3 \text{ g}}{1 \text{kg}} \times \dfrac{1 \text{ mol C}_8\text{H}_{18}}{114.22 \text{ g}} \times \dfrac{16 \text{ mol CO}_2}{2 \text{ mol C}_8\text{H}_{18}} \times \dfrac{44.01 \text{ g}}{1 \text{ mol CO}_2} \times \dfrac{1 \text{ kg}}{1000 \text{ g}}$

$= 2 \times 10^{13} \text{ kg CO}_2$

$(2 \times 10^{13} \text{kg CO}_2)(X \text{ years}) = 3 \times 10^{15} \text{kg CO}_2 \Rightarrow X = 150 \text{ years}$

Electrons in Atoms
and the Periodic Table

Questions

1. Both the Bohr model and the quantum-mechanical model were developed in the early 1900s. These models serve to explain how electrons are arranged within the atomic structure and how the electrons affect the chemical and physical properties of each element.

3. The speed of light is 3.0×10^8 m/s or 186,000 miles/s. Light could travel around the world in 1/7 of a second.

5. When we look at a blue object, it appears blue because the object reflects the wavelength corresponding to blue and absorbs all of the other wavelengths from the white light that illuminated the object.

7. The longer the wavelength, the smaller the frequency and vice versa (an inverse relationship).

9. X-rays are used to image internal bones and organs.

11. The ultraviolet rays, which cause sunburn and suntan, also have the ability to damage biological molecules. UV rays are linked to skin cancer, cataracts, and premature skin wrinkling.

13. Only certain molecules, such as water, can absorb microwaves. This explains why your food, which contains water, is heated while your plate, which doesn't contain water, does not heat.

15. The Bohr model for hydrogen places the single electron in a circular orbit around the nucleus. The orbit of the electron is quantized. That is, it has a fixed energy at a specific fixed distance from the nucleus.

17. The Bohr model orbit is a circular orbit that maps the exact path an electron would make around a nucleus. The quantum mechanical model however has an orbital that is best described as a region that has the greatest probability for the location of an electron.

19. The four subshells are *s*, *p*, *d* and *f*. The maximum number of electrons are 2, 6, 10, and 14, respectively.

21. The Pauli exclusion principle says that the maximum number of electrons in an orbital is two. The two electrons must have opposite spin direction to occupy the same orbital. This is important in assigning electron configurations, as it allows you to determine how and where the electrons should be assigned.

23. [Ne] represents $1s^2 2s^2 2p^6$
    [Kr] represents $1s^2 2s^2 2p^6 3s^2 3p^6 4s^2 3d^{10} 4p^6$

25.

27. Group 1 elements form +1 ions because the electron configuration of the ion will match that of a noble gas. The group 7 elements form -1 ions for the same reason.

Problems

Wavelength, Energy, and Frequency of Electromagnetic Radiation

29. c) infrared

31. radiowaves < microwaves < infrared < ultraviolet

33. Two of the following three: gamma rays, X-rays, or ultraviolet rays.

35. a) X-rays
    b) X-rays
    c) microwave

The Bohr Model

37. Bohr orbits have fixed <u>energies</u> and fixed <u>distances</u>.

39. The smaller the wavelength the larger the energy of the photon. Therefore, the 410 nm wavelength corresponds to the $n=6$ to $n=2$ transition and the 434 nm wavelength corresponds to the $n=5$ to $n=2$ transition.

The Quantum-mechanical Model

41. The 2s and 3p would have the same shape as the 1s and 2p. The only difference is that they would be larger in size.

43. On average, the 2s electron is closer to the nucleus, because it is in a smaller orbital.

45. The transition with the smallest energy difference will produce the longer wavelength. This would correspond to the 2p to 1s transition.

Electron Configurations

47. a) $1s^2 2s^2 2p^2$
    b) $1s^2 2s^2 2p^6 3s^1$
    c) $1s^2 2s^2 2p^6 3s^2 3p^6$
    d) $1s^2 2s^2 2p^6 3s^2 3p^2$

49.

51. a) $[Ar]4s^2 3d^{10} 4p^1$
    b) $[Ar]4s^2 3d^{10} 4p^3$
    c) $[Kr]5s^1$
    d) $[Kr]5s^2 4d^{10} 5p^2$

53. a) $[Ar]4s^2 3d^2$
    b) $[Ar]4s^2 3d^3$
    c) $[Ar]4s^1 3d^5$
    d) $[Ar]4s^2 3d^6$

Valence Electrons and Core Electrons

55. Valence electrons are <u>underlined</u>.
    a) $1s^2 \underline{2s^2 2p^1}$
    b) $1s^2 \underline{2s^2 2p^3}$
    c) $1s^2 2s^2 2p^6 3s^2 3p^6 4s^2 3d^{10} 4p^6 \underline{5s^2} 4d^{10} \underline{5p^3}$
    d) $1s^2 2s^2 2p^6 3s^2 3p^6 \underline{4s^1}$

57. a) 6
    b) 6
    c) 7
    d) 1

Electron Configurations and the Periodic Table

59. a) ns^1
    b) ns^2
    c) $ns^2 np^3$
    d) $ns^2 np^5$

61. a) $[Ne]3s^2 3p^1$
    b) $[He]2s^2$
    c) $[Kr]5s^2 4d^{10} 5p^1$
    d) $[Kr]5s^2 4d^2$

63. a) $[Ar]4s^2 3d^{10} 4p^3$
    b) $[Xe]6s^2$
    c) $[Ar]4s^2 3d^8$
    d) $[Xe]6s^2 4f^{14} 5d^{10} 6p^3$

65. a) 2
    b) 3
    c) 5
    d) 6

67. a) 8
    b) 8
    c) 18
    d) 18

69. a) aluminum
    b) sulfur
    c) argon
    d) magnesium

71. a) chlorine
    b) gallium
    c) iron
    d) rubidium

Periodic Trends

73. a) Na
    b) Ge
    c) cannot determine based on periodic properties alone
    d) P

75. Pb < Sn < Te < S < Cl

77. a) In
    b) Si
    c) Pb
    d) C

79. F < S < Si < Ge < Ca < Rb

81. a) Sr
    b) Bi
    c) cannot determine based on periodic properties alone
    d) As

83. S < Se < Sb < In < Ba < Fr

Cumulative Problems

85. The alkali metals all share the [ ]ns^1 electron configuration. By losing one electron to form the +1 ion, the electron configuration of the ion becomes the same as a noble gas.

87. a) $1s^2 2s^2 2p^6 3s^2 3p^6$
    b) $1s^2 2s^2 2p^6 3s^2 3p^6$
    c) $1s^2 2s^2 2p^6 3s^2 3p^6$
    d) $1s^2 2s^2 2p^6 3s^2 3p^6 4s^2 3d^{10} 4p^6$

89. Metals are on the left side of the periodic table because they tend to give up electrons to form positive ions, which assume an electron configuration identical to that of a noble gas. Nonmetals are on the right side of the periodic table because they tend to gain electrons to form negative ions, which assume an electron configuration identical to that of a noble gas. The metalloids are the boundary region between the metals and nonmetals.

91. a) There is a maximum of 6 p and 2 s electrons for any principle quantum number.
$1s^2 2s^2 2p^6 3s^2 3p^3$
b) There is not a $2d$ subshell.
$1s^2 2s^2 2p^6 3s^2 3p^2$
c) There is not a $1p$ subshell.
$1s^2 2s^2 2p^2$
d) There is a maximum of 6 p electrons for any principle quantum number.
$1s^2 2s^2 2p^6 3s^2 3p^3$

93. The electron configuration of bromine shows that it is one electron short of having the same electron configuration of argon, a noble gas. Therefore bromine is very reactive because it wants to obtain a full outer shell of electrons as the noble gases already have. Krypton is a noble gas that already has a full outer shell, therefore there is no advantage to undergoing any reactions.

95. $E = \dfrac{hc}{\lambda} \Rightarrow \lambda = \dfrac{hc}{E} = \dfrac{(6.626 \times 10^{-34}\, J \cdot s)(3.00 \times 10^8\, m/s)}{3.0 \times 10^{-19}\, J} = 6.6 \times 10^{-7}\, m$

97. $1.496 \times 10^8\, km \times \dfrac{1 \times 10^3\, m}{1\, km} \times \dfrac{1\, s}{3.00 \times 10^8\, m} = 498.7s = 8.31\, min = 8\, min\ 19\, sec$

99. The quantum-mechanical model provided the ability to understand and predict chemical bonding, which is the basic level of understanding of matter and how it interacts. This model was critical in the areas of lasers, computers, drug design and semiconductors. The quantum-mechanical model for the atom is considered the foundation of modern chemistry.

101. a) $E = \dfrac{hc}{\lambda} = \dfrac{(6.626x10^{-34}\,J\cdot s)(2.99x10^{8}\,m/s)}{1500\ nm \times \dfrac{1\ m}{1x10^{9}\,nm}} = 1.3x10^{-19}\,J$ per photon

$\dfrac{1.3x10^{-19}\,J}{photon} \times \dfrac{1\ kJ}{1x10^{3}\,J} \times \dfrac{6.022x10^{23}\,photons}{1\ mole} = 80\ kJ/mol,\ No.$

b) $E = \dfrac{hc}{\lambda} = \dfrac{(6.626x10^{-34}\,J\cdot s)(2.99x10^{8}\,m/s)}{500\ nm \times \dfrac{1\ m}{1x10^{9}\,nm}} = 4.0x10^{-19}\,J$ per photon

$\dfrac{4.0x10^{-19}\,J}{photon} \times \dfrac{1\ kJ}{1x10^{3}\,J} \times \dfrac{6.022x10^{23}\,photons}{1\ mole} = 239\ kJ/mol,\ No.$

c) $E = \dfrac{hc}{\lambda} = \dfrac{(6.626x10^{-34}\,J\cdot s)(2.99x10^{8}\,m/s)}{150\ nm \times \dfrac{1\ m}{1x10^{9}\,nm}} = 1.3x10^{-18}\,J$ per photon

$\dfrac{1.3x10^{-18}\,J}{photon} \times \dfrac{1\ kJ}{1x10^{3}\,J} \times \dfrac{6.022x10^{23}\,photons}{1\ mole} = 800\ kJ/mol,\ Yes.$

Chemical Bonding

Questions

1. Bonding theories are important because they allow us to accurately predict how atoms bond together to form molecules.

3. Ne=$1s^22s^22p^6$, 8 valence electrons
   Ar=$1s^22s^22p^63s^23p^6$, 8 valence electrons

5. A chemical bond in the Lewis theory is the sharing or transfer of electrons between atoms, which allows the atoms to obtain a stable electron configuration (an octet).

7. The Lewis structure for potassium has one valence electron, while the Lewis structure for monoatomic chlorine has seven valence electrons. From these structures we can determine that if potassium gives up the one valence electron to chlorine, K^+ and Cl^- are formed. Therefore, the formula must be KCl.

9. A double bond is shorter and stronger than a single bond. A triple bond is shorter and even stronger than a double bond or a single bond.

11. Add up the valence electrons from each atom that is forming the molecule.

13. The octet rule has exceptions because the theory is not 100% accurate; however, it does work well in a majority of cases. Some exceptions to the rules are compounds that have odd numbers of valence electrons, boron compounds that tend to form with only six valence electrons, and some compounds that have more than eight valence electrons.

15. The valence shell electron pair repulsion (VSEPR) theory states that molecular shape is dictated by the fact that electron pairs, whether lone pairs or bonding pairs, repel each other and try to assume an optimum maximum distance from each other.

17. a) 180°
    b) 120°
    c) 109.5°

19. Electronegativity is the ability of an atom to attract electrons toward itself in a covalent bond.

72

21. A polar covalent bond is a covalent bond in which electrons are not equally shared between the two atoms.

23. It is extremely important to know if a molecule is polar or non-polar because polarity dictates how molecules interact with each other.

25. If a molecule has polar bonds, it will depend on the geometry of the molecule to determine if the polar bonds cancel each other out or not.

Problems

Writing Lewis Structures for Elements

25. N: $1s^2 2s^2 2p^3$, ·N̈: , the 2s and 2p electrons were used.

27. a) K·

   b) Ål:

   c) ·P̈:

   d) :Ä̈r:

29. :Ẍ: Halogens tend to gain one electron in reactions.

31. M: Alkaline earth metals tend to lose two electrons in reactions.

33. a) [:C̈l:]⁻

   b) [:S̈e:]⁻²

   c) Na⁺

   d) Mg⁺²

Lewis Structures for Ionic Compounds

35. a) Na⁺ [:F̈:]⁻

   b) Ca⁺² [:Ö:]⁻²

   c) [:B̈r:]⁻ Sr⁺² [:B̈r:]⁻

   d) K⁺ [:Ö:]⁻² K⁺

37. a) SrSe
    b) $BaCl_2$
    c) Na_2S
    d) Al_2O_3

39. a) Li^+ $[:\ddot{F}:]^-$

    b) Li^+ $[:\ddot{O}:]^{-2}$ Li^+

    c) Li^+ $[:\ddot{N}:]^{-3}$ Li^+

    Li^+

41. a) Cs^+ $[:\ddot{Cl}:]^-$

    b) Ba^{+2} $[:\ddot{O}:]^{-2}$

    c) $[:\ddot{I}:]^-$ Ca^{+2} $[:\ddot{I}:]^-$

Lewis Structures for Covalent Compounds

43. a) H—$\ddot{P}$—H
    |
    H

    b) :$\ddot{Cl}$—$\ddot{S}$—$\ddot{Cl}$:

    c) :$\ddot{F}$—$\ddot{F}$:

    d) H—$\ddot{I}$:

45. a) $\ddot{O}$=$\ddot{O}$

    b) :C≡ O:

    c) H—$\ddot{O}$—$\ddot{N}$=$\ddot{O}$ or H—$\ddot{O}$=$\ddot{N}$—$\ddot{O}$:

    d) $\ddot{O}$=$\ddot{S}$—$\ddot{O}$: ↔ :$\ddot{O}$—$\ddot{S}$=$\ddot{O}$

47. a) H—C≡ C—H

    b) H—C=C—H
       | |
       H H

    c) H—$\ddot{N}$=$\ddot{N}$—H

    d) H—$\ddot{N}$—$\ddot{N}$—H
       | |
       H H

74

49. a) :N ≡ N:

b) S̈=Si=S̈

c) H—Ö—H

d) :Ï— N̈ —Ï:
        :Ï:

51. a) Ö=S̈e—Ö: ↔ :Ö—S̈e=O

b) $\left[\ddot{O} = C - \ddot{O}: \atop :\ddot{O}: \right]^{-2}$ ↔ $\left[:\ddot{O} - C = \ddot{O} \atop :\ddot{O}: \right]^{-2}$ ↔ $\left[:\ddot{O} - C - \ddot{O}: \atop \ddot{O}: \right]^{-2}$

c) $\left[:\ddot{C}l - \ddot{O}: \right]^{-}$

d) $\left[:\ddot{O} - \ddot{C}l - \ddot{O}: \right]^{-}$

53. a) $\left[:\ddot{O} - P - \ddot{O}: \atop :\ddot{O}: \right]^{-3}$ (with :Ö: on top)

b) $\left[:C ≡ N: \right]^{-}$

c) $\left[\ddot{O} = \dot{N} - \ddot{O}: \right]^{-}$ ↔ $\left[:\ddot{O} - \dot{N} = \ddot{O} \right]^{-}$

d) $\left[:\ddot{O} - S - \ddot{O}: \atop :\ddot{O}: \right]^{-2}$

55. a) :C̈l—B— C̈l:
        :C̈l:

b) Ö=Ṅ—Ö: ↔ :Ö—Ṅ= Ö

c) H— B—H
     H

Predicting the Shapes of Molecules

57. a) 4
    b) 4
    c) 4
    d) 2

59. a) 3 bonding groups, 1 lone pair
    b) 2 bonding groups, 2 lone pairs
    c) 4 bonding groups, 0 lone pairs
    d) 2 bonding groups, 0 lone pairs

61. a) tetrahedral
    b) trigonal planar
    c) linear
    d) trigonal planar

63. a) 109.5°
    b) 120°
    c) 180°
    d) 120°

65. a) electron geometry = linear
       molecular geometry = linear
    b) electron geometry = trigonal planar
       molecular geometry = bent
    c) electron geometry = tetrahedral
       molecular geometry = bent
    d) electron geometry = tetrahedral
       molecular geometry = trigonal pyramidal

67. a) 180°
    b) 120°
    c) 109.5°
    d) 109.5°

69. a) electron geometry = linear
       molecular geometry = linear
    b) Both nitrogen atoms have identical electron and molecular geometry.
       electron geometry = trigonal planar
       molecular geometry = bent
    c) Both nitrogen atoms have identical electron and molecular geometry.
       electron geometry = tetrahedral
       molecular geometry = trigonal pyramidal

71. a) trigonal planar
     b) bent
     c) trigonal planar
     d) tetrahedral

Electronegativity and Polarity

73. a) 1.2
     b) 1.8
     c) 2.8

75. a) 2.8 – 1.2 = 1.6, polar covalent
     b) 4.0 – 1.6 = 2.4, ionic
     c) 2.8 – 2.8 = 0, pure covalent
     d) 3.5 – 1.8 = 1.7, polar covalent

77. a) polar, different electronegativities
     b) nonpolar, same electronegativities
     c) nonpolar, same electronegativities
     d) polar, different electronegativities

79. a) nonpolar, The C and S atoms have identical electronegativities.
     b) polar
     c) nonpolar, The C and H atoms have different electronegativities, but symmetry cancels the effect.
     d) polar

81. a) nonpolar, The B and H atoms have different electronegativities, but symmetry cancels the effect.
     b) polar
     c) nonpolar, The C and H atoms have different electronegativities, but symmetry cancels the effect.
     d) polar

Cumulative Problems

83. a) Ca: $1s^2 2s^2 2p^6 3s^2 3p^6 \underline{4s^2}$, Ca:

     b) Ga: $1s^2 2s^2 2p^6 3s^2 3p^6 \underline{4s^2} 3d^{10} \underline{4p^1}$, Ġa:

     c) As: $1s^2 2s^2 2p^6 3s^2 3p^6 \underline{4s^2} 3d^{10} \underline{4p^3}$, ·Ȧs:

     d) I: $1s^2 2s^2 2p^6 3s^2 3p^6 4s^2 3d^{10} 4p^6 \underline{5s^2} 4d^{10} \underline{5p^5}$, :Ï:

85. a) ionic, K^+ $\left[:\ddot{\underset{..}{S}}: \right]^{-2}$ K^+

    b) covalent, $H—\underset{\underset{\displaystyle :\ddot{F}:}{|}}{C}=\ddot{O}$

    c) ionic, Mg^{+2} $\left[:\ddot{\underset{..}{Se}}: \right]^{-2}$

    d) covalent, $:\ddot{\underset{..}{Br}}—\underset{\underset{\displaystyle :\ddot{Br}:}{|}}{P}—\ddot{\underset{..}{Br}}:$

87. $\ddot{O}=\underset{\underset{\displaystyle :\ddot{C}l:}{|}}{C}—\ddot{C}l:$

    The 3-D shape should be trigonal planar.

89. $H—\underset{\underset{\displaystyle H}{|}}{\overset{\overset{\displaystyle H}{|}}{C}}—\overset{\overset{\displaystyle :O:}{||}}{C}—\ddot{O}—H$

    The 3-D shape of the molecule has the first carbon in a tetrahedral shape, the second carbon in a trigonal planar shape, and the single-bonded oxygen in a bent shape.

91. $H:\ddot{C}l: + Na^+ \left[:\ddot{O}—H \right]^- \rightarrow H—\ddot{O}—H + Na^+ \left[:\ddot{\underset{..}{C}l}: \right]^-$

93. a) $K^+ \left[:\ddot{O}—H \right]^-$

    b) $K^+ \left[:\ddot{O}—\underset{\underset{\displaystyle :\ddot{O}:}{|}}{N}=\ddot{O} \right]^- \leftrightarrow K^+ \left[\ddot{O}=\underset{\underset{\displaystyle :\ddot{O}:}{|}}{N}—\ddot{O}: \right]^- \leftrightarrow K^+ \left[:\ddot{O}—\underset{\underset{\displaystyle :O:}{||}}{N}—\ddot{O}: \right]^-$

    c) $Li^+ \left[:\ddot{I}—\ddot{O}: \right]^-$

    d) $Ba^{+2} \left[:\ddot{O}—\underset{\underset{\displaystyle :\ddot{O}:}{|}}{C}=\ddot{O} \right]^{-2} \leftrightarrow Ba^{+2} \left[\ddot{O}=\underset{\underset{\displaystyle :\ddot{O}:}{|}}{C}—\ddot{O}: \right]^{-2} \leftrightarrow Ba^{+2} \left[:\ddot{O}—\underset{\underset{\displaystyle :O:}{||}}{C}—\ddot{O}: \right]^{-2}$

Highlight Problems

95. a) $\left[:\ddot{O}\!-\!\dot{O}: \right]^{-}$

b) $\left[:\ddot{O}: \right]^{-}$

c) $:\ddot{O}\!-\!H$

d) $H\!-\!\underset{\underset{H}{|}}{\overset{\overset{H}{|}}{C}}\!-\!\ddot{O}\!-\!\dot{O}\cdot$

97. a) incorrect; The structure should have bent molecular geometry.
b) correct
c) incorrect; The structure should have trigonal pyramidal geometry.
d) correct

Gases

11

Questions

1. Pressure is the force per unit area that is caused by gaseous molecules as they collide with a surface.

3. The upper limit of a straw is about 10.3 meters.

5. • Gases are compressible. This is because of the large distance between gas particles.
   • Gases assume the shape and volume of their container. This is because gas particles are in constant, straight line motion.
   • Gases have low densities as compared with solids and liquids. This is because there is a large distance between particles that is filled with only empty space.

7. The main units to measure pressure are the atmosphere (atm), the pascal (Pa), the millimeters of mercury (mmHg), and the torr.

9. If the volume of a gas container decreases, the same number of gas particles are crowded in a smaller volume, which causes more collisions with the container wall.

11. Extra long snorkels would not work because the pressure of the air on the surface is at about 1 atm of pressure while the air in a divers lung is at high pressure (10 m depth = 2 atm pressure). If you connected the diver with a snorkel at the surface, the high pressure in the lungs would force all of the air out to the surface, opposite of what you want!

13. The kinetic molecular theory supports Charles's law because as the temperature increases, the gas particles will move faster. If the pressure is to remain unchanged, the volume of the gas would have to increase.

15. The combined gas law is $\dfrac{P_1 V_1}{T_1} = \dfrac{P_2 V_2}{T_2}$. This law is used when two variables are changed at once.

17. Avogadro's law is supported by the kinetic molecular theory because if you have more gas particles and the pressure and temperature remain unchanged, the particles must be occupying a larger volume.

19. The ideal gas law is most accurate under the conditions of low pressure and high temperature. It breaks down at high pressures and low temperatures. This breakdown occurs because the gases are no longer acting according to the kinetic molecular theory. The gas particles start interacting (attraction and repulsion), and the distance between gas particles is no longer large.

21. Dalton's law of partial pressure is: $P_{tot} = P_1 + P_2 + P_3 + ...$

23. Deep-sea divers use a helium-oxygen mixture to prevent oxygen toxicity and nitrogen narcosis.

25. The vapor pressure is the partial pressure of water in a mixture. The vapor pressure is temperature dependent.

Problems

Converting Between Pressure Units

27. a) $879 \text{ torr} \times \dfrac{1 \text{ atm}}{760 \text{ torr}} = 1.16 \text{ atm}$

   b) $19.5 \text{ psi} \times \dfrac{1 \text{ atm}}{14.7 \text{ psi}} = 1.33 \text{ atm}$

   c) $30.07 \text{ in Hg} \times \dfrac{1 \text{ atm}}{29.92 \text{ in Hg}} = 1.005 \text{ atm}$

   d) $98.4 x 10^3 \text{Pa} \times \dfrac{1 \text{ atm}}{101,325 \text{ Pa}} = 0.971 \text{ atm}$

29. a) $2.3 \text{ atm} \times \dfrac{760 \text{ torr}}{1 \text{ atm}} = 1.7 x 10^3 \text{ torr}$

   b) $4.7 x 10^{-2} \text{atm} \times \dfrac{760 \text{ mm Hg}}{1 \text{ atm}} = 36 \text{ mm Hg}$

   c) $24.8 \text{ psi} \times \dfrac{760 \text{ mm Hg}}{14.7 \text{ psi}} = 1.28 x 10^3 \text{ mm Hg}$

   d) $32.84 \text{ in Hg} \times \dfrac{760 \text{ torr}}{29.92 \text{ in Hg}} = 834.2 \text{ torr}$

31. a) $24.9 \text{ in Hg} \times \dfrac{1 \text{ atm}}{29.92 \text{ in Hg}} = 0.832 \text{ atm}$

b) $24.9 \text{ in Hg} \times \dfrac{760 \text{ mm Hg}}{29.92 \text{ in Hg}} = 632 \text{ mm Hg}$

c) $24.9 \text{ in Hg} \times \dfrac{14.7 \text{ psi}}{29.92 \text{ in Hg}} = 12.2 \text{ psi}$

d) $24.9 \text{ in Hg} \times \dfrac{101,325 \text{ Pa}}{29.92 \text{ in Hg}} = 8.43 x 10^4 \text{ Pa}$

33. a) $31.85 \text{ in Hg} \times \dfrac{760 \text{ mm Hg}}{29.92 \text{ in Hg}} = 809.0 \text{ mm Hg}$

b) $31.85 \text{ in Hg} \times \dfrac{1 \text{ atm}}{29.92 \text{ in Hg}} = 1.065 \text{ atm}$

c) $31.85 \text{ in Hg} \times \dfrac{760 \text{ torr}}{29.92 \text{ in Hg}} = 809.0 \text{ torr}$

d) $31.85 \text{ in Hg} \times \dfrac{101,325 \text{ Pa}}{29.92 \text{ in Hg}} \times \dfrac{1 \text{ kPa}}{1000 \text{ Pa}} = 107.9 \text{ kPa}$

Simple Gas Laws

35. $P_1 = 755 \text{mm Hg}$, $V_1 = 2.8 \text{ L}$, $V_2 = 3.7 \text{ L}$, $P_2 = ?$; $P_1 V_1 = P_2 V_2$

$(755 \text{mm Hg})(2.8 \text{ L}) = (3.7 \text{ L})(P_2) \Rightarrow P_2 = \dfrac{(755 \text{mm Hg})(2.8 \text{ L})}{(3.7 \text{ L})} = 5.7 x 10^2 \text{mm Hg}$

37. $P_1 = 1.0 \text{ atm}$, $V_1 = 6.3 \text{ L}$, $V_2 = ? \text{ L}$, $P_2 = 3.5 \text{ atm}$; $P_1 V_1 = P_2 V_2$

$(1.0 \text{ atm})(6.3 \text{ L}) = (V_2)(3.5 \text{ atm}) \Rightarrow V_2 = \dfrac{(1.0 \text{ atm})(6.3 \text{ L})}{(3.5 \text{ atm})} = 1.8 \text{ L}$

39. $T_1 = 305 \text{ K}$, $V_1 = 3.8 \text{ L}$, $T_2 = 385 \text{ K}$, $V_2 = ?$; $\dfrac{V_1}{T_1} = \dfrac{V_2}{T_2}$

$\dfrac{3.8 \text{ L}}{305 \text{ K}} = \dfrac{V_2}{385 \text{ K}} \Rightarrow V_2 = \dfrac{(3.8 \text{ L})(385 \text{ K})}{(305 \text{ K})} = 4.8 \text{ L}$

41. $T_1 = 22 + 273 = 295$ K, $V_1 = 48.3$ mL, $T_2 = 87 + 273 = 360$ K, $V_2 = ?$; $\dfrac{V_1}{T_1} = \dfrac{V_2}{T_2}$

$$\frac{48.3 \text{ mL}}{295 \text{ K}} = \frac{V_2}{360 \text{ K}} \Rightarrow V_2 = \frac{(48.3 \text{ mL})(360 \text{ K})}{(295 \text{ K})} = 58.9 \text{ mL}$$

43. $n_1 = 0.15$ mol, $V_1 = 3.42$ L, $n_2 = 0.25$ mol, $V_2 = ?$; $\dfrac{V_1}{n_1} = \dfrac{V_2}{n_2}$

$$\frac{3.42 \text{ L}}{0.15 \text{ mol}} = \frac{V_2}{0.25 \text{ mol}} \Rightarrow V_2 = \frac{(3.42 \text{ L})(0.25 \text{ mol})}{(0.15 \text{ mol})} = 5.7 \text{ L}$$

45. $n_1 = 0.128$ mol, $V_1 = 2.76$ L, $n_2 = 0.128 + 0.073 = 0.201$ mol, $V_2 = ?$; $\dfrac{V_1}{n_1} = \dfrac{V_2}{n_2}$

$$\frac{2.76 \text{ L}}{0.128 \text{ mol}} = \frac{V_2}{0.201 \text{ mol}} \Rightarrow V_2 = \frac{(2.76 \text{ L})(0.201 \text{ mol})}{(0.128 \text{ mol})} = 4.33 \text{ L}$$

Combined Gas Law

47. $P_1 = 755$ mm Hg, $V_1 = 32.5$ L, $T_1 = 315$ K, $P_2 = ?$, $V_2 = 15.8$ L, $T_2 = 395$ K

$$\frac{P_1 V_1}{T_1} = \frac{P_2 V_2}{T_2} \Rightarrow \frac{(755 \text{ mm Hg})(32.5 \text{ L})}{(315 \text{ K})} = \frac{(P_2)(15.8 \text{ L})}{(395 \text{ K})} \Rightarrow$$

$$P_2 = \frac{(755 \text{ mm Hg})(32.5 \text{ L})(395 \text{ K})}{(315 \text{ K})(15.8 \text{ L})} = 1.95 \times 10^3 \text{ mm Hg}$$

49. $P_1 = 1.0$ atm, $V_1 = 2.8$ L, $T_1 = 34 + 273 = 307$ K,

$P_2 = 3.5$ atm, $V_2 = ?$, $T_2 = 18 + 273 = 291$ K

$$\frac{P_1 V_1}{T_1} = \frac{P_2 V_2}{T_2} \Rightarrow \frac{(1.0 \text{ atm})(2.8 \text{ L})}{(307 \text{ K})} = \frac{(3.5 \text{ atm})(V_2)}{(291 \text{ K})} \Rightarrow$$

$$V_2 = \frac{(1.0 \text{ atm})(2.8 \text{ L})(291 \text{ K})}{(307 \text{ K})(3.5 \text{ atm})} = 0.76 \text{ L}$$

51. P_1=735 mm Hg, T_1=28+273=301 K, P_2=?, T_2=86+273=359 K

$$\frac{P_1}{T_1}=\frac{P_2}{T_2} \Rightarrow \frac{(735 \text{ mm Hg})}{(301\text{ K})}\times\frac{(P_2)}{(359\text{ K})} \Rightarrow P_2 = \frac{(735\text{ mm Hg})(359\text{ K})}{(301\text{ K})}=$$

877mm Hg

53. P=0.97 atm, V=?, n=0.118 mol, T=305 K, PV=nRT

$$(0.97\text{ atm})(V)=(0.118\text{ mol}) (0.0821\frac{L\cdot atm}{mol\cdot K})(305\text{ K}) \Rightarrow$$

$$V=\frac{(0.118\text{ mol}) (0.0821\frac{L\cdot atm}{mol\cdot K})(305\text{ K})}{(0.97\text{ atm})} = 3.0\text{ L}$$

55. P=1.8 atm, V=28.5 L, n=?, T=298 K, PV=nRT

$$(1.8\text{ atm})(28.5\text{ L})=(n) (0.0821\frac{L\cdot atm}{mol\cdot K})(298\text{ K}) \Rightarrow$$

$$n=\frac{(1.8\text{ atm})(28.5\text{ L})}{(0.0821\frac{L\cdot atm}{mol\cdot K})(298\text{ K})} = 2.1\text{ mol}$$

57. $P=43.2\text{ psi}\times\frac{1\text{ atm}}{14.7\text{ psi}}=2.94$ atm, V=11.8 L, n=?, T=25+273=298 K

$$PV=nRT \Rightarrow (2.94\text{ atm})(11.8\text{ L})=(n)(0.0821\frac{L\cdot atm}{mol\cdot K})(298\text{ K}) \Rightarrow$$

$$n=\frac{(2.94\text{ atm})(11.8\text{ L})}{(0.0821\frac{L\cdot atm}{mol\cdot K})(298\text{ K})}=1.42\text{ mol}$$

59. $P = 24.1 \text{ psi} \times \dfrac{1 \text{ atm}}{14.7 \text{ psi}} = 1.64 \text{ atm}$, V=3.5 L, n=?, T=25+273=298 K

$$PV = nRT \Rightarrow (1.64 \text{ atm})(3.5 \text{ L}) = (n)(0.0821 \dfrac{\text{L} \cdot \text{atm}}{\text{mol} \cdot \text{K}})(298 \text{ K}) \Rightarrow$$

$$n = \dfrac{(1.64 \text{ atm})(3.5 \text{ L})}{(0.0821 \dfrac{\text{L} \cdot \text{atm}}{\text{mol} \cdot \text{K}})(298 \text{ K})} = 0.23 \text{ mol}$$

61. $P = 745 \text{ mm Hg} \times \dfrac{1 \text{ atm}}{760 \text{ mm Hg}} = 0.980 \text{ atm}$, $V = 248 \text{ mL} \times \dfrac{1 \text{ L}}{1000 \text{ mL}} = 0.248 \text{ L}$,

n=?, T=28+273=301 K

$$PV = nRT \Rightarrow (0.980 \text{ atm})(0.248 \text{ L}) = (n)(0.0821 \dfrac{\text{L} \cdot \text{atm}}{\text{mol} \cdot \text{K}})(301 \text{ K}) \Rightarrow$$

$$n = \dfrac{(0.980 \text{ atm})(0.248 \text{ L})}{(0.0821 \dfrac{\text{L} \cdot \text{atm}}{\text{mol} \cdot \text{K}})(301 \text{ K})} = 0.00983 \text{ mol}$$

$$\text{molar mass} = \dfrac{0.433 \text{ g}}{0.00983 \text{ mol}} = 44.0 \text{ g/mol}$$

63. $P = 886 \text{ torr} \times \dfrac{1 \text{ atm}}{760 \text{ torr}} = 1.17 \text{ atm}$, $V = 224 \text{ mL} \times \dfrac{1 \text{ L}}{1000 \text{ mL}} = 0.224 \text{ L}$,

n=?, T=55+273=328 K

$$PV = nRT \Rightarrow (1.17 \text{ atm})(0.224 \text{ L}) = (n)(0.0821 \dfrac{\text{L} \cdot \text{atm}}{\text{mol} \cdot \text{K}})(328 \text{ K}) \Rightarrow$$

$$n = \dfrac{(1.17 \text{ atm})(0.224 \text{ L})}{(0.0821 \dfrac{\text{L} \cdot \text{atm}}{\text{mol} \cdot \text{K}})(328 \text{ K})} = 0.00973 \text{ mol}$$

$$\text{molar mass} = \dfrac{38.8 \text{ mg} \times \dfrac{1 \text{ g}}{1000 \text{ mg}}}{0.00973 \text{ mol}} = 4.00 \text{ g/mol}$$

Partial Pressure

65. $P_{tot} = P_1 + P_2 + P_3 + \ldots \Rightarrow P_{tot} = 355 + 128 + 229 = 712$ torr

67. $P_{tot} = P_{He} + P_{O_2} \Rightarrow 11.0$ atm $= P_{He} + 0.30$ atm $\Rightarrow P_{He} = 11.0 - 0.30 = 10.7$ atm

69. $P_{tot} = P_{H_2} + P_{H_2O} \Rightarrow 732$ mm Hg $= P_{H_2} + 31.8$

   $P_{H_2} = 732 - 31.8 = 700$ mm Hg

71. $P_{N_2} = 1.12$ atm $\times 0.78 = 0.87$ atm $P_{O_2} = 1.12$ atm $\times 0.22 = 0.25$ atm

73. $P_{O_2} = 8.5$ atm $\times 0.04 = 0.34$ atm

Molar Volume

75. a) 2.5 mol He $\times \dfrac{22.4 \text{ L}}{1 \text{ mol He}} = 56$ L

   b) 5.9 mol $N_2 \times \dfrac{22.4 \text{ L}}{1 \text{ mol } N_2} = 1.3 x 10^2$ L

   c) 32.7 mol $Cl_2 \times \dfrac{22.4 \text{ L}}{1 \text{ mol } Cl_2} = 732$ L

   d) 41 mol $CH_4 \times \dfrac{22.4 \text{ L}}{1 \text{ mol } CH_4} = 9.2 x 10^2$ L

77. a) 73.9 g $N_2 \times \dfrac{1 \text{ mol } N_2}{28.02 \text{ g}} \times \dfrac{22.4 \text{ L}}{1 \text{ mol } N_2} = 59.1$ L

   b) 42.9 g $O_2 \times \dfrac{1 \text{ mol } O_2}{32.00 \text{ g}} \times \dfrac{22.4 \text{ L}}{1 \text{ mol } O_2} = 30.0$ L

   c) 148 g $NO_2 \times \dfrac{1 \text{ mol } NO_2}{46.01 \text{ g}} \times \dfrac{22.4 \text{ L}}{1 \text{ mol } NO_2} = 72.1$ L

   d) 245 mg $CO_2 \times \dfrac{1 \text{ g}}{1000 \text{ mg}} \times \dfrac{1 \text{ mol } CO_2}{44.01 \text{ g}} \times \dfrac{22.4 \text{ L}}{1 \text{ mol } CO_2} = 0.125$ L

79. $178 \text{ ml } CO_2 \times \dfrac{1 \text{ L}}{1000 \text{ mL}} \times \dfrac{1 \text{ mol } CO_2}{22.4 \text{ L}} \times \dfrac{44.01 \text{ g}}{1 \text{ mol } CO_2} = 0.350 \text{ g}$

Gases in Chemical Reactions

81. $n = 1.45 \text{ mol C} \times \dfrac{1 \text{ mol } H_2}{1 \text{ mol C}} = 1.45 \text{ mol } H_2$, P=1.0 atm, T=355K, V=?

$PV = nRT \Rightarrow (1.0 \text{ atm})(V) = (1.45 \text{ mol})(0.0821 \dfrac{L \cdot atm}{mol \cdot K})(355 \text{ K}) \Rightarrow$

$V = \dfrac{(1.45 \text{ mol})(0.0821 \dfrac{L \cdot atm}{mol \cdot K})(355 \text{ K})}{(1.0 \text{ atm})} = 42 \text{ L}$

83. $P = 748 \text{ mm Hg} \times \dfrac{1 \text{ atm}}{760 \text{ mm Hg}} = 0.984 \text{ atm}$, V=?, T=86+273=359K

$n = 0.55 \text{ mol } CH_3OH \times \dfrac{2 \text{ mol } H_2}{1 \text{ mol } CH_3OH} = 1.1 \text{ mol } H_2$

$PV = nRT \Rightarrow (0.984 \text{ atm})(V) = (1.1 \text{mol})(0.0821 \dfrac{L \cdot atm}{mol \cdot K})(359 \text{ K}) \Rightarrow$

$V = \dfrac{(1.1 \text{mol})(0.0821 \dfrac{L \cdot atm}{mol \cdot K})(359 \text{ K})}{(0.984 \text{ atm})} = 33 \text{ L of } H_2$

Because the molar ratio of CO to H_2 is 1:2, we can simply divide the volume of H_2 in half to determine CO. Volume of CO=33/2=17 L

Warning this only works for gases! It does not apply to volumes of liquids or masses of solids in a reaction.

85. $P = 892 \text{ torr} \times \dfrac{1 \text{ atm}}{760 \text{ torr}} = 1.17 \text{ atm}$, V=?, T=95+273=368 K

$n = 18.5 \text{ g Al} \times \dfrac{1 \text{ mol Al}}{26.98 \text{ g}} \times \dfrac{1 \text{ mol } N_2}{2 \text{ mol Al}} = 0.343 \text{ mol } N_2$

85. (cont.)

$$PV=nRT \Rightarrow (1.17 \text{ atm})(V)=(0.343 \text{ mol})(0.0821 \frac{\text{L} \cdot \text{atm}}{\text{mol} \cdot \text{K}})(368 \text{ K}) \Rightarrow$$

$$V=\frac{(0.343 \text{ mol})(0.0821 \frac{\text{L} \cdot \text{atm}}{\text{mol} \cdot \text{K}})(368 \text{ K})}{(1.17 \text{ atm})} = 8.83 \text{ L}$$

87. $24.8 \text{ L H}_2 \times \dfrac{1 \text{ mol H}_2}{22.4 \text{ L}} \times \dfrac{2 \text{ mol NH}_3}{3 \text{ mol H}_2} \times \dfrac{17.03 \text{ g}}{1 \text{ mol NH}_3} = 12.6 \text{ g NH}_3$

89. $156.8 \text{ mL O}_2 \times \dfrac{1 \text{ L}}{1000 \text{ mL}} \times \dfrac{1 \text{ mol O}_2}{22.4 \text{ L}} \times \dfrac{2 \text{ mol Ca}}{1 \text{ mol O}_2} \times \dfrac{40.08 \text{ g}}{1 \text{ mol Ca}} = 0.561 \text{ g Ca}$

Cumulative Problems

91. P=1.00 atm, V=?, n=1.00 mol, T=273 K

$$V=\frac{(1.00 \text{ mol})(0.0821 \frac{\text{L} \cdot \text{atm}}{\text{mol} \cdot \text{K}})(273 \text{ K})}{(1.00 \text{ atm})} = 22.4 \text{L}$$

93. $P=267 \text{ torr} \times \dfrac{1 \text{ atm}}{760 \text{ torr}} = 0.351 \text{ atm}$, $V=255 \text{ mL} \times \dfrac{1 \text{ L}}{1000 \text{ mL}} = 0.255 \text{ L}$,

n=?, T=25+273=298 K, mass=143.289 – 143.187=0.102 g

$$PV=nRT \Rightarrow (0.351 \text{ atm})(0.255 \text{ L})=(n)(0.0821 \frac{\text{L} \cdot \text{atm}}{\text{mol} \cdot \text{K}})(298\text{K})$$

$$n=\frac{(0.351 \text{ atm})(0.255 \text{ L})}{(0.0821 \frac{\text{L} \cdot \text{atm}}{\text{mol} \cdot \text{K}})(298\text{K})}=0.00366 \text{ moles}$$

$$\text{molar mass} = \frac{0.102 \text{ g}}{0.00366 \text{ moles}} = 27.9 \text{ g/mol}$$

95. $P=556 \text{ mm Hg} \times \dfrac{1 \text{ atm}}{760 \text{ mm Hg}} = 0.732 \text{ atm}, \quad V=158 \text{ mL} \times \dfrac{1 \text{ L}}{1000 \text{ mL}} = 0.158 \text{ L},$

n=?, T=25+273=298 K, mass=0.275 g

$PV=nRT \Rightarrow (0.732 \text{ atm})(0.158 \text{ L})=(n)(0.0821\dfrac{\text{L} \cdot \text{atm}}{\text{mol} \cdot \text{K}})(298\text{K})$

$n=\dfrac{(0.732 \text{ atm})(0.158 \text{ L})}{(0.0821\dfrac{\text{L} \cdot \text{atm}}{\text{mol} \cdot \text{K}})(298\text{K})} = 0.00473 \text{ moles}$

$\text{molar mass} = \dfrac{0.275 \text{ g}}{0.00473 \text{ moles}} = 58.1 \text{ g/mol}$

In one mole of compound,

$\text{mass C}=58.1 \times 0.8266 = 48.0 \text{ g} \Rightarrow 48.0 \times \dfrac{1 \text{ mole C}}{12.01 \text{ g}} = 4 \text{ mol C}$

$\text{mass H}=58.1 \times 0.1734 = 10.1 \text{ g} \Rightarrow 10.1 \text{ g} \times \dfrac{1 \text{ mol H}}{1.008 \text{ g}} = 10 \text{ mol H}$

Molecular formula: C_4H_{10}

97. $P_{tot} = P_{H_2O} + P_{H_2} \Rightarrow 748 \text{ mm Hg}=23.8 + P_{H_2} \Rightarrow P_{H_2} = 748 - 23.8 = 724 \text{ mm Hg}$

$P=724 \text{ mm Hg} \times \dfrac{1 \text{ atm}}{760 \text{ mm Hg}} = 0.953 \text{ atm}, \quad T=25+273=298\text{K}, \quad n=?$

$V=325 \text{ mL} \times \dfrac{1 \text{ L}}{1000 \text{ mL}} = 0.325 \text{ L}$

$PV=nRT \Rightarrow (0.953 \text{ atm})(0.325 \text{ L})=(n)(0.0821\dfrac{\text{L} \cdot \text{atm}}{\text{mol} \cdot \text{K}})(298 \text{ K})$

$n=\dfrac{(0.953 \text{ atm})(0.325 \text{ L})}{(0.0821\dfrac{\text{L} \cdot \text{atm}}{\text{mol} \cdot \text{K}})(298 \text{ K})} = 0.0127 \text{ mol H}_2$

$0.0127 \text{ mol H}_2 \times \dfrac{1 \text{ mol Zn}}{1 \text{ mol H}_2} \times \dfrac{65.39 \text{ g}}{1 \text{ mol Zn}} = 0.855$

99. $P_{tot} = P_{H_2O} + P_{H_2} \Rightarrow 748\ torr = 55.3 + P_{H_2} \Rightarrow P_{H_2} = 748 - 55.3 = 693\ torr$

$P = 693\ mm\ Hg \times \dfrac{1\ atm}{760\ mm\ Hg} = 0.912\ atm,\ T = 40 + 273 = 313\ K,\ V = 1.78\ L,\ n = ?$

$PV = nRT \Rightarrow (0.912\ atm)(1.78\ L) = (n)(0.0821\dfrac{L \cdot atm}{mol \cdot K})(313\ K)$

$n = \dfrac{(0.912\ atm)(1.78\ L)}{(0.0821\dfrac{L \cdot atm}{mol \cdot K})(313\ K)} = 0.0632\ mol\ H_2$

$0.0632\ mol\ H_2 \times \dfrac{1.008\ g}{1\ mol\ H_2} = 0.0636\ g$

101. $P_{tot} = P_{H_2O} + P_{O_2} \Rightarrow 752\ mm\ Hg = 23.8 + P_{O_2} \Rightarrow P_{O_2} = 752 - 23.8 = 728\ mm\ Hg$

$P = 728\ torr \times \dfrac{1\ atm}{760\ mm\ Hg} = 0.958\ atm,\ T = 25 + 273 = 298\ K,\ V = ?$

$n = 15.8\ g\ Ag \times \dfrac{1\ mol\ Ag}{107.9\ g} \times \dfrac{1\ mol\ O_2}{4\ mol\ Ag} = 0.0366\ mol$

$PV = nRT \Rightarrow (0.958\ atm)(V) = (0.0366)(0.0821\dfrac{L \cdot atm}{mol \cdot K})(298\ K)$

$V = \dfrac{(0.0366)(0.0821\dfrac{L \cdot atm}{mol \cdot K})(298\ K)}{(0.958\ atm)} = 0.935\ L$

103. a) $285.5\ mL\ SO_2 \times \dfrac{1\ L}{1000\ mL} \times \dfrac{1\ mol\ SO_2}{22.4\ L} \times \dfrac{2\ mol\ SO_3}{2\ mol\ SO_2} = 0.0127\ mol\ SO_3$

$158.9\ mL\ O_2 \times \dfrac{1\ L}{1000\ mL} \times \dfrac{1\ mol\ O_2}{22.4\ L} \times \dfrac{2\ mol\ SO_3}{1\ mol\ O_2} = 0.0142\ mol\ SO_3$

The limiting reactant is SO_2 and the theoretical yield of SO_3 is 0.0127 mol.

b) $187.2\ mL\ SO_3 \times \dfrac{1\ L}{1000\ mL} \times \dfrac{1\ mol\ SO_3}{22.4\ L} = 0.00836\ mol\ SO_3$

$Percent\ Yield = \dfrac{Actual}{Theoretical} \times 100\% \Rightarrow \dfrac{0.00836}{0.0127} \times 100\% = 65.8\%$

105. a) $12.8 \text{ L } NO_2 \times \dfrac{1 \text{ mol } NO_2}{22.4 \text{ L}} \times \dfrac{2 \text{ mol } HNO_3}{3 \text{ mol } NO_2} = 0.381 \text{ mol } HNO_3$

$14.9 \text{ g } H_2O \times \dfrac{1 \text{ mol } H_2O}{18.02 \text{ g}} \times \dfrac{2 \text{ mol } HNO_3}{1 \text{ mol } H_2O} = 1.65 \text{ mol } HNO_3$

The limiting reactant is NO_2.

$\text{Mass } HNO_3 = 0.381 \text{ mol } HNO_3 \times \dfrac{63.02 \text{ g}}{1 \text{ mol } HNO_3} = 24.0 \text{ g } HNO_3$

b) $\text{Percent Yield} = \dfrac{\text{Actual}}{\text{Theoretical}} \times 100\% \Rightarrow \dfrac{14.8}{24.0} \times 100\% = 61.7\%$

Highlight Problems

107. Choice c will have the greatest pressure because it has the highest number of gas particles that can collide with the container walls to create pressure.

109. $11.8 \text{ L} \times \dfrac{1 \text{ mol } N_2}{22.4 \text{ L}} \times \dfrac{2 \text{ mol } NaN_3}{3 \text{ mol } N_2} \times \dfrac{65.02 \text{ g}}{1 \text{ mol } NaN_3} = 22.8 \text{ g } NaN_3$

Liquids, Solids, and Intermolecular Forces

12

Questions

1. The bitter taste is due to the interaction of molecules with receptors on the surface of specialized cells on the tongue.

3. Intermolecular forces are the reason why solids and liquids exist, and they have other effects such as determining protein and DNA shape.

5. The relative magnitude of the intermolecular forces to thermal energy determine whether a substance is a solid, liquid, or gas.

7. Properties of Solids:
    a) Solids have high densities in comparison to gases.
    b) Solids have a definite shape; they do not assume the shape of their container.
    c) Solids have a definite volume; they are not easily compressed.
    d) Solids may be crystalline (ordered) or amorphous (disordered).

9. Properties of Solids:
    a) Solids have high densities in comparison to gases.
       The solid particles are in close contact, where gas particles are not.
    b) Solids have a definite shape; they do not assume the shape of their container.
       The solid particles are in fixed positions.
    c) Solids have a definite volume; they are not easily compressed.
       The solid particles are in close contact.

11. Surface tension is the tendency of liquids to minimize their surface area due to the interaction of molecules between each other. The surface tension increases when intermolecular forces increase.

13. Evaporation is when a liquid undergoes a physical change to a gas. Condensation is the physical change when a gaseous substance changes to a liquid form.

15. The process of evaporation below the boiling point only occurs at the surface of the liquid. At the boiling point, there is sufficient thermal energy that molecules within the interior of the liquid can break free and enter into the gas phase.

17. The intermolecular forces in acetone are weaker, therefore it evaporates faster and is the more volatile compound.

19. Vapor pressure is the partial pressure of a gas in dynamic equilibrium with its liquid. The vapor pressure of a compound increases with increasing temperature and decreases with increasing strength of the intermolecular forces.

21. The process of condensation is the opposite of evaporation in that it is exothermic. This means that energy is released from the gas as it forms a liquid. Steam at 100° releases more heat into your hand due to condensation than water at the same temperature.

23. The process of freezing is exothermic which releases heat from the water into the freezer. If the freezer cannot remove the excess heat, the freezer will start to warm up and the water will not freeze.

25. Dispersion force (aka London Force) is a type of intermolecular force present between all molecules and atoms. This type of intermolecular force arises from fluctuations in the spacial distribution of electrons in the atom or molecule that causes a temporary positive and negative within a particle. The dispersion force increases with increasing molar mass.

27. The hydrogen bond occurs when hydrogen bonds to either F, O, or N (very electronegative), which in turn pulls the shared electrons in the bond away from hydrogen. Hydrogen becomes very positive and forms a hydrogen bond to the lone pair electrons on F, O or N of another molecule. Compounds that can form hydrogen bonds will have higher melting and boiling points than other compounds that do not form hydrogen bonds.

29. Molecular solids have low to moderately low melting points.

31. The melting points of ionic solids tend be much higher than molecular solids.

33. Water is unique because it has a low molar mass and is a liquid at room temperature, which is not the case with other low molar mass compounds. Additionally, while most compounds contract during the freezing process, water expands. This is the reason ice floats on water.

Problems

Evaporation, Condensation, Melting, and Freezing

35. The second beaker of 55 mL in a 12 cm diameter dish will evaporate more quickly because evaporation occurs at the surface and the 12 cm dish has a larger surface area.

37. Acetone will feel cooler because it has weaker intermolecular forces, which makes it more volatile.

39. The temperature will increase from $^-5°C$ to the melting point at $0°C$. The temperature will not increase until all of the ice has melted. After the ice has completely melted, the temperature will increase until it reaches room temperature ($25°C$).

41. The steam would cause a more severe burn because steam condensation is an exothermic process and this excess heat would increase the severity of the burn.

43. The water in the bag is undergoing the freezing process, which releases heat (exothermic) into the rest of the cooler.

45. The ice chest full of ice at $0°C$ would be colder because in order to melt the ice, heat from the cooler would be absorbed (endothermic). The ice chest full of water at $0°C$ would be warmer because the freezing process releases heat (exothermic) and would warm the cooler.

47. The boiling point occurs when the vapor pressure of the liquid is equal to the external pressure, which shows that the atmospheric pressure is less than 1 atm in Denver.

Heat of Vaporization and Heat of Fusion

49. $34.8 \text{ g } H_2O \times \dfrac{1 \text{ mol } H_2O}{18.02 \text{ g}} \times \dfrac{40.6 \text{ kJ}}{1 \text{ mol } H_2O} = 78.4 \text{ kJ}$

51. $2.8 \text{ g } H_2O \times \dfrac{1 \text{ mol } H_2O}{18.02 \text{ g}} \times \dfrac{44.0 \text{ kJ}}{1 \text{ mol } H_2O} = 6.8 \text{ kJ}$

53. $2.56 \text{ g } H_2O \times \dfrac{1 \text{ mol } H_2O}{18.02 \text{ g}} \times \dfrac{44.0 \text{ kJ}}{1 \text{ mol } H_2O} = 6.25 \text{ kJ}$

55. $835 \text{ kJ} \times \dfrac{1 \text{ mol } H_2O}{40.6 \text{ kJ}} \times \dfrac{18.02 \text{ g}}{1 \text{ mol } H_2O} = 371 \text{ g } H_2O$

57. $28.9 \text{ g } H_2O \times \dfrac{1 \text{ mol } H_2O}{18.02 \text{ g}} \times \dfrac{6.02 \text{ kJ}}{1 \text{ mol } H_2O} = 9.65 \text{ kJ}$

59. $47.5 \text{ g } H_2O \times \dfrac{1 \text{ mol } H_2O}{18.02 \text{ g}} \times \dfrac{6.02 \text{ kJ}}{1 \text{ mol } H_2O} = 15.9 \text{ kJ}$

61. a) dispersion
    b) dispersion
    c) dispersion, dipole-dipole
    d) dispersion, hydrogen bond

63. a) dispersion, dipole-dipole
    b) dispersion, dipole-dipole, hydrogen bond
    c) dispersion
    d) dispersion

65. Choice d would have the highest boiling point because it has a larger molar mass, which indicates stronger dispersion forces.

67. The CH_3OH compound will be a liquid at room temperature because it will have hydrogen bonding, dipole-dipole, and dispersion intermolecular forces, while CH_3SH would contain only dipole-dipole and dispersion intermolecular forces.

69. The first liquid that would start to form is NH_3 because of its ability to form hydrogen bonds. CH_4 cannot form hydrogen bonds, so condensation would not start until a much lower temperature was reached.

71. No, $CH_3CH_2CH_2CH_2CH_3$ is nonpolar where H_2O is polar and they are not miscible.

Types of Solids

73. a) atomic
    b) molecular
    c) ionic
    d) atomic

75. a) molecular
    b) ionic
    c) molecular
    d) molecular

77. Choice c because ionic compounds tend to have high melting points due to the strong electrostatic attraction present in the solid.

79. a) Ti(s) has a higher melting point because metallic atomic solids have stronger metallic bonds compared to the weak dispersion force that holds together non-bonding atomic solids like Ne(s).

b) $H_2O(s)$ has a higher melting point because of hydrogen bonds, which are not found in H_2S.

c) Xe(s) has a higher melting point because of stronger dispersion forces found in larger atoms.

d) NaCl(s) has a higher melting point because electrostatic attraction in ionic solids is stronger than intermolecular forces in covalent solids.

Cumulative Problems

81. a) $58 \text{ g } H_2O \times \dfrac{1 \text{ mol } H_2O}{18.02 \text{ g}} \times \dfrac{6.02 \text{ kJ}}{1 \text{ mol } H_2O} \times \dfrac{1000 \text{ J}}{1 \text{ kJ}} = 1.9x10^4 \text{ J}$

b) $1.9x10^4 \text{ J} \times \dfrac{1 \text{ kJ}}{1000 \text{ J}} = 19 \text{ kJ}$

c) $1.9x10^4 \text{ J} \times \dfrac{1 \text{ cal}}{4.18 \text{ J}} = 4.5x10^3 \text{ cal}$

d) $4.5x10^3 \text{ cal} \times \dfrac{1 \text{ Cal}}{1000 \text{ cal}} = 4.5 \text{ Cal}$

83. $8.5 \text{ g } H_2O \times \dfrac{1 \text{ mol } H_2O}{18.02 \text{ g}} \times \dfrac{6.02 \text{ kJ}}{1 \text{ mol } H_2O} \times \dfrac{1000 \text{ J}}{1 \text{ kJ}} = 2.8x10^3 \text{ J}$

$2.8x10^3 \text{ J} = 255 \text{g} \times 4.18 \text{J/g} \cdot °C \times \Delta T$

$\Delta T = \dfrac{2.8x10^3 \text{ J}}{255 \text{g} \times 4.18 \text{J/g} \cdot °C} = 2.7°C$

85. $q = 352 \text{g} \times 4.18 \text{J/g} \cdot °C \times 20°C = 2.94x10^4 \text{ J}$

$2.94x10^4 \text{ J} \times \dfrac{1 \text{ kJ}}{1000 \text{ J}} \times \dfrac{1 \text{ mol } H_2O}{6.02 \text{ kJ}} \times \dfrac{18.02 \text{ g}}{1 \text{ mol } H_2O} = 88.1 \text{ g } H_2O$

87. a) H—S̈e—H Bent Geometry, Dispersion & Dipole-Dipole Forces

b) Ö=S̈—Ö: Bent Geometry, Dispersion & Dipole-Dipole Forces

c)
$$\begin{array}{c} :\ddot{C}l: \\ | \\ H - C - \ddot{C}l: \\ | \\ :\ddot{C}l: \end{array}$$
Tetrahedral Geometry, Dispersion & Dipole-Dipole Forces

d) Ö=C=Ö Linear Geometry, Dispersion Force

89. $Na^+ \left[:\ddot{F}: \right]^- \quad Mg^{+2} \left[:\ddot{O}: \right]^{-2}$

Because the strength of a +2 to -2 attraction is stronger than a +1 to -1, MgO has the higher melting point.

Highlight Problems

91. Interior molecules have the most neighbors. The surface molecule is more likely to evaporate. The number of neighbors would change; however, surface molecules will always have less than interior molecules and will always be more likely to evaporate.

93. a) This is a valid criticism because ice displaces more volume than the liquid water that makes it up. The melting of ice in a cup would actually result in a small decrease in volume.
b) The melting of ice from the continent would increase ocean levels because this water is not currently in the ocean itself.

Solutions

13

Questions

1. A solution is a homogeneous mixture of two or more substances.

3. The solvent is the major component of the solution. The solute is the minor component in the solution. An example is soda pop where carbon dioxide and sugar are solutes and water is the solvent. Another example is salt water, in which salt is the solute and water is the solvent.

5. Solubility is the amount of a compound (grams) that will dissolve in a specified amount of a solvent.

7. A strong electrolyte solution is one that will conduct electricity due to the dissociation of ionic species in solution. A nonelectrolyte solution will not conduct electricity due to the absence of ions in solution. Ionic compounds tend to form strong electrolytes and molecular compounds form nonelectrolyte solutions.

9. Recrystallization is the process in which a solid is dissolved in a suitable solvent, usually at elevated temperatures. As the solution cools, it becomes supersaturated, and the excess solid begins to come out of solution.

11. The bubbles that form in water when it is heated to a temperature lower than the boiling point are dissolved gases that are coming out of solution. The solubility of gases decreases as a function of increased temperatures.

13. The solubility of gases increases with increasing pressure.

15. A dilute solution is one that contains a small amount of solute relative to the solvent. A concentrated solution is one that contains a large amount of solute relative to the solvent.

17. Molarity is defined as the number of moles of solute per liter of solution.

19. The addition of a nonvolatile solute will lower the freezing point and raise the boiling point of a solution relative to that of the pure solvent.

21. Molality is defined as the moles of solute dissolved per kilogram of solvent.

23. By drinking seawater, the one survivor created a region of high salt concentration on the outside of the cells in his body. This caused osmosis of water out of the cells in the body into the saltwater he had consumed, causing more severe dehydration.

Problems

Solutions

25. a) not a solution
    b) not a solution
    c) solution
    d) solution (Sterling silver is a solid solution of 925 parts Ag and 75 parts Cu.)

27. a) solvent: water, solute: salt
    b) solvent: water, solute: sugar
    c) solvent: water, solute: soda

29. a) hexane, ethyl ether, or toluene
    b) water, acetone, or methyl alcohol
    c) hexane, ethyl ether, or toluene

Solids Dissolved in Water

31. The dissolved particles are the cations and anions that make up the ionic solute. This solution is referred to as a strong electrolyte.

33. unsaturated

35. recrystallization

Gases Dissolved in Water

37. The solubility of gases decreases as temperature increases. When water is boiled, the dissolved oxygen is completely removed.

39. The solubility of gases (nitrogen) increases with increasing pressure. The diver could prevent this effect either by not diving as deep or by using a helium-oxygen mixture as discussed in Chapter 11.

Mass Percent

41. a) mass % = $\dfrac{12.8 \text{ g NaCl}}{(12.8 + 145) \text{ g solution}} \times 100\% = 8.11\%$

b) mass % = $\dfrac{55.1 \text{ g } C_{12}H_{22}O_{11}}{(55.1 + 478) \text{ g solution}} \times 100\% = 10.3\%$

c) mass % = $\dfrac{355 \text{ mg } C_{12}H_{22}O_{11} \times \dfrac{1 \text{ g}}{1000 \text{ mg}}}{\left(355 \text{ mg} \times \dfrac{1 \text{ g}}{1000 \text{ mg}} + 5.22\right) \text{ g solution}} \times 100\% = 6.37\%$

43. mass % = $\dfrac{45 \text{ g sugar}}{(45 + 309) \text{ g solution}} \times 100\% = 13\%$

45. $\dfrac{3.5 \text{ g NaCl}}{100 \text{ g solution}} \times 274 \text{ g solution} = 9.3 \text{ g NaCl}$

47. a) $\dfrac{4.9 \text{ g sucrose}}{100 \text{ g solution}} \times 55 \text{ g solution} = 2.7 \text{ g sucrose}$

b) $\dfrac{11.2 \text{ mg sucrose}}{100 \text{ mg solution}} \times 122 \text{ mg solution} = 13.7 \text{ mg sucrose}$

c) $\dfrac{17.1 \text{ kg sucrose}}{100 \text{ kg solution}} \times 5.8 \text{ kg solution} = 0.99 \text{ kg sucrose}$

49. a) $1.5 \text{ g NaCl} \times \dfrac{100 \text{ g solution}}{0.045 \text{ g NaCl}} = 3.3x10^3 \text{ g solution}$

b) $1.5 \text{ g NaCl} \times \dfrac{100 \text{ g solution}}{1.94 \text{ g NaCl}} = 77 \text{ g solution}$

c) $1.5 \text{ g NaCl} \times \dfrac{100 \text{ g solution}}{9.82 \text{ g NaCl}} = 15 \text{ g solution}$

51. mass of AgCl solution: $4.8 \text{ L} \times \dfrac{1000 \text{ mL}}{1 \text{ L}} \times \dfrac{1.01 \text{ g}}{1 \text{ mL}} = 4.8 x 10^{3} \text{ g}$

$4.8 x 10^{3} \text{ g solution} \times \dfrac{3.4 \text{ g Ag}}{100 \text{ g solution}} = 1.6 x 10^{2} \text{ g Ag}$

53. $45.8 \text{ g NaCl} \times \dfrac{100 \text{ g solution}}{3.5 \text{ g NaCl}} = 1.3 x 10^{3} \text{ g solution}$

55. $150 \text{ mg Pb} \times \dfrac{1 \text{ g}}{1000 \text{ mg}} \times \dfrac{100 \text{ g solution}}{0.0011 \text{ g Pb}} \times \dfrac{1 \text{ ml}}{1 \text{ g}} = 1.4 x 10^{4} \text{ g solution}$

Molarity

57. a) $\text{M} = \dfrac{1.3 \text{ mol KCl}}{2.5 \text{ L}} = 0.52 \text{ M KCl}$

b) $\text{M} = \dfrac{0.225 \text{ mol KNO}_3}{0.855 \text{ L}} = 0.263 \text{ M KNO}_3$

c) $\text{M} = \dfrac{0.117 \text{ mol sucrose}}{588 \text{ mL} \times \dfrac{1 \text{ L}}{1000 \text{ mL}}} = \dfrac{0.117 \text{ mol sucrose}}{0.588 \text{ L}} = 0.199 \text{ M sucrose}$

59. a) moles: $22.6 \text{ g C}_{12}\text{H}_{22}\text{O}_6 \times \dfrac{1 \text{ mol C}_{12}\text{H}_{22}\text{O}_6}{342.30 \text{ g}} = 0.660 \text{ mol C}_{12}\text{H}_{22}\text{O}_6$

$\text{M} = \dfrac{0.660 \text{ mol C}_{12}\text{H}_{22}\text{O}_6}{1.58 \text{ L}} = 0.461 \text{ M C}_{12}\text{H}_{22}\text{O}_6$

b) moles: $42.6 \text{ g NaCl} \times \dfrac{1 \text{ mol NaCl}}{58.44 \text{ g}} = 0.729 \text{ mol NaCl}$

$\text{M} = \dfrac{0.729 \text{ mol NaCl}}{0.442 \text{ L}} = 1.65 \text{ M NaCl}$

59. (cont.)

c) moles: $315 \text{ mg } C_6H_{12}O_6 \times \dfrac{1 \text{ g}}{1 \times 10^3 \text{ mg}} \times \dfrac{1 \text{ mol } C_6H_{12}O_6}{180.16 \text{ g}} \Rightarrow$

$= 1.75 \times 10^{-3} \text{ mol } C_6H_{12}O_6$

liters: $58.2 \text{ mL} \times \dfrac{1 \text{ L}}{1000 \text{ mL}} = 0.0582 \text{ L}$

$M = \dfrac{1.75 \times 10^{-3} \text{ mol } C_6H_{12}O_6}{0.0582 \text{ L}} = 0.0300 \text{ M } C_6H_{12}O_6$

61. moles: $7.2 \text{ g NaCl} \times \dfrac{1 \text{ mol NaCl}}{58.44 \text{ g}} = 0.12 \text{ mol NaCl}$

liters: $205 \text{ mL} \times \dfrac{1 \text{ L}}{1000 \text{ mL}} = 0.205 \text{ mL}$

$M = \dfrac{0.12 \text{ mol NaCl}}{0.205 \text{ L}} = 0.60 \text{ M NaCl}$

63. a) $\dfrac{1.2 \text{ mol NaCl}}{L} \times 1.5 \text{ L} = 1.8 \text{ mol NaCl}$

b) $\dfrac{0.85 \text{ mol NaCl}}{L} \times 0.448 \text{ L} = 0.38 \text{ mol NaCl}$

c) $\dfrac{1.65 \text{ mol NaCl}}{L} \times 144 \text{ mL} \times \dfrac{1 \text{ L}}{1000 \text{ mL}} = 0.238 \text{ mol NaCl}$

65. a) $0.10 \text{ mol KCl} \times \dfrac{1 \text{ L}}{0.255 \text{ mol KCl}} = 0.39 \text{ L}$

b) $0.10 \text{ mol KCl} \times \dfrac{1 \text{ L}}{1.8 \text{ mol KCl}} = 0.056 \text{ L}$

c) $0.10 \text{ mol KCl} \times \dfrac{1 \text{ L}}{0.995 \text{ mol KCl}} = 0.10 \text{ L}$

67. $55 \text{ mL} \times \dfrac{1 \text{ L}}{1000 \text{ mL}} \times \dfrac{1.5 \text{ mol NaCl}}{1 \text{ L}} \times \dfrac{58.44 \text{ g}}{1 \text{ mol NaCl}} = 4.8 \text{ g NaCl}$

102

69. $2.5 \text{ L} \times \dfrac{0.100 \text{ mol KCl}}{1 \text{ L}} \times \dfrac{74.55 \text{ g}}{1 \text{ mol KCl}} = 19 \text{ g KCl}$

71. $1.5 \text{ kg } C_{12}H_{22}O_{11} \times \dfrac{1000 \text{ g}}{1 \text{ kg}} \times \dfrac{1 \text{ mol } C_{12}H_{22}O_{11}}{342.3 \text{ g}} \times \dfrac{1 \text{ L}}{0.500 \text{ mol}} = 8.8 \text{ L}$

Solution Dilution

73. $M_1 V_1 = M_2 V_2 \Rightarrow (1.2 \text{ M})(158 \text{ mL}) = (M_2)(500 \text{ mL})$

$M_2 = \dfrac{(1.2 \text{ M})(158 \text{ mL})}{(500 \text{ mL})} = 0.38 \text{ M}$

75. $M_1 V_1 = M_2 V_2 \Rightarrow (5.5 \text{ M})(V_1) = (0.100 \text{ M})(2.5 \text{ L})$

$V_1 = \dfrac{(0.100 \text{ M})(2.5 \text{ L})}{(5.5 \text{ M})} = 0.045 \text{ L}$

You would dilute 45 mL (0.045 L) of the 5.5 M stock solution to a final volume of 2.5 L.

77. $M_1 V_1 = M_2 V_2 \Rightarrow (12 \text{ M})(25 \text{ mL}) = (0.500 \text{ M})(V_2)$

$V_2 = \dfrac{(12 \text{ M})(25 \text{ mL})}{(0.500 \text{ M})} = 6.0 \times 10^2 \text{ mL}$

79. $M_1 V_1 = M_2 V_2 \Rightarrow (12.0 \text{ M})(V_1) = (0.250 \text{ M})(850.0 \text{ mL})$

$V_1 = \dfrac{(0.250 \text{ M})(850.0 \text{ mL})}{(12.0 \text{ M})} = 17.7 \text{ mL}$

Solution Stoichiometry

81. a) $\dfrac{0.150 \text{ mol HCl}}{1 \text{ L}} \times 25 \text{ mL} \times \dfrac{1 \text{ L}}{1000 \text{ mL}} \times \dfrac{1 \text{ mol NaOH}}{1 \text{ mol HCl}} \times \dfrac{1 \text{ L}}{0.150 \text{ mol NaOH}}$

$= 0.025 \text{ L}$

b) $\dfrac{0.055 \text{ mol HCl}}{1 \text{ L}} \times 55 \text{ mL} \times \dfrac{1 \text{ L}}{1000 \text{ mL}} \times \dfrac{1 \text{ mol NaOH}}{1 \text{ mol HCl}} \times \dfrac{1 \text{ L}}{0.150 \text{ mol NaOH}}$

$= 0.020 \text{ L}$

81. (cont.)

c) $\dfrac{0.885 \text{ mol HCl}}{1 \text{ L}} \times 175 \text{ mL} \times \dfrac{1 \text{ L}}{1000 \text{ mL}} \times \dfrac{1 \text{ mol NaOH}}{1 \text{ mol HCl}} \times \dfrac{1 \text{ L}}{0.150 \text{ mol NaOH}}$

$= 1.03 \text{ L}$

83. $\dfrac{0.0112 \text{ mol NiCl}_2}{1 \text{ L}} \times 134 \text{ mL} \times \dfrac{1 \text{ L}}{1000 \text{ mL}} \times \dfrac{2 \text{ mol K}_3\text{PO}_4}{3 \text{ mol NiCl}_2} \times \dfrac{1 \text{ L}}{0.225 \text{ mol K}_3\text{PO}_4}$

$= 0.00445 \text{ L}$

85. $\dfrac{0.100 \text{ mol KOH}}{1 \text{ L}} \times 112 \text{ mL} \times \dfrac{1 \text{ L}}{1000 \text{ mL}} \times \dfrac{1 \text{ mol H}_3\text{PO}_4}{3 \text{ mol KOH}} \times \dfrac{1}{10.0 \text{ ml}} \times \dfrac{1000 \text{ ml}}{1 \text{ L}}$

$= 0.373 \text{ M H}_3\text{PO}_4$

87. $15.0 \text{ g H}_2 \times \dfrac{1 \text{ mol H}_2}{2.016 \text{ g}} \times \dfrac{3 \text{ mol H}_2\text{SO}_4}{3 \text{ mol H}_2} \times \dfrac{1 \text{ L}}{6.0 \text{ mol H}_2\text{SO}_4} = 1.2 \text{ L}$

89. a) $m = \dfrac{0.25 \text{ mol}}{0.250 \text{ kg}} = 1.0 \text{ m}$

b) $m = \dfrac{0.882 \text{ mol}}{0.225 \text{ kg}} = 3.92 \text{ m}$

c) $m = \dfrac{0.012 \text{ mol}}{23.1 \text{ g}} \times \dfrac{1000 \text{ g}}{1 \text{ kg}} = 0.52 \text{ m}$

91. $11.5 \text{ g C}_2\text{H}_6\text{O}_2 \times \dfrac{1 \text{ mol C}_2\text{H}_6\text{O}_2}{62.07 \text{ g}} \times \dfrac{1}{145 \text{ g H}_2\text{O}} \times \dfrac{1000 \text{ g}}{1 \text{ kg}} = 1.28 \text{ m C}_2\text{H}_6\text{O}_2$

93. a) $\Delta T_f = 0.85 \dfrac{\text{mol}}{\text{kg}} \times 1.86 \dfrac{°\text{C} \cdot \text{kg}}{\text{mol}} = 1.6°\text{C} \Rightarrow \text{Freezing Point} = -1.6°\text{C}$

b) $\Delta T_f = 1.45 \dfrac{\text{mol}}{\text{kg}} \times 1.86 \dfrac{°\text{C} \cdot \text{kg}}{\text{mol}} = 2.70°\text{C} \Rightarrow \text{Freezing Point} = -2.70°\text{C}$

94. (cont.)

c) $\Delta T_f = 4.8 \dfrac{mol}{kg} \times 1.86 \dfrac{°C \cdot kg}{mol} = 8.9°C \Rightarrow$ Freezing Point = -8.9°C

d) $\Delta T_f = 2.35 \dfrac{mol}{kg} \times 1.86 \dfrac{°C \cdot kg}{mol} = 4.37°C \Rightarrow$ Freezing Point = -4.37°C

95. a) $\Delta T_b = 0.118 \dfrac{mol}{kg} \times 0.512 \dfrac{°C \cdot kg}{mol} = 0.0604°C \Rightarrow$ Boiling Point = 100.060°C

b) $\Delta T_b = 1.94 \dfrac{mol}{kg} \times 0.512 \dfrac{°C \cdot kg}{mol} = 0.993°C \Rightarrow$ Boiling Point = 100.993°C

c) $\Delta T_b = 3.88 \dfrac{mol}{kg} \times 0.512 \dfrac{°C \cdot kg}{mol} = 1.99°C \Rightarrow$ Boiling Point = 101.99°C

d) $\Delta T_b = 2.16 \dfrac{mol}{kg} \times 0.512 \dfrac{°C \cdot kg}{mol} = 1.11°C \Rightarrow$ Boiling Point = 101.11°C

97. molality: $55.8 \ g \ C_6H_{12}O_6 \times \dfrac{1 \ mol \ C_6H_{12}O_6}{180.2 \ g} \times \dfrac{1}{455 \ g} \times \dfrac{1000 \ g}{1 \ kg} = 0.681 \ m$

$\Delta T_f = 0.681 \dfrac{mol}{kg} \times 1.86 \dfrac{°C \cdot kg}{mol} = 1.27°C$

Freezing Point = 0.00 − 1.27 = −1.27°C

$\Delta T_b = 0.681 \dfrac{mol}{kg} \times 0.512 \dfrac{°C \cdot kg}{mol} = 0.349°C$

Boiling Point = 100.000 + 0.349 = 100.349°C

Cumulative Problems

99. Molarity: $133 \ g \ NaCl \times \dfrac{1 \ mol \ NaCl}{58.44 \ g} \times \dfrac{1}{1.00 \ L} = 2.28 \ M$

Mass Percent: $\dfrac{133 \ g}{1.00 \ L \times \dfrac{1000 \ ml}{1 \ L} \times \dfrac{1.08 \ g}{1 \ mL}} = 12.3\%$

101. $(8.5 \text{ M})(0.125 \text{ L})=(M_2)(2.5 \text{ L}) \Rightarrow M_2 = \dfrac{(8.5 \text{ M})(0.125 \text{ L})}{(2.5 \text{ L})} = 0.43 \text{ M}$

$10.8 \text{ g NaCl} \times \dfrac{1 \text{ mol NaCl}}{58.44 \text{ g}} \times \dfrac{1 \text{ L}}{0.43 \text{ mol NaCl}} = 0.43 \text{ L}$

103. $3.25 \text{ g KI} \times \dfrac{1 \text{ mol KI}}{166.0 \text{ g}} \times \dfrac{1}{0.0250 \text{ L}} = 0.783 \text{ M KI}$

$(5.00 \text{ M})(50.00 \text{ mL})=(0.783 \text{ M})(V_2) \Rightarrow V_2 = \dfrac{(5.00 \text{ M})(50.00 \text{ mL})}{(0.783 \text{ M})}$

$=319 \text{ mL}$

105. $15.0 \text{ L H}_2 \times \dfrac{1 \text{ mol H}_2}{22.4 \text{ L}} \times \dfrac{3 \text{ mol H}_2SO_4}{3 \text{ mol H}_2} \times \dfrac{1 \text{ L}}{4.0 \text{ mol}} = 0.17 \text{ L}$

107. $58.5 \text{ g C}_2H_6O_2 \times \dfrac{1 \text{ mol C}_2H_6O_2}{62.07 \text{ g}} \times \dfrac{1}{500.0 \text{ mL}} \times \dfrac{1 \text{ mL}}{1.09 \text{ g}} \times \dfrac{1000 \text{ g}}{1 \text{ kg}} = 1.73 \text{ m}$

$\Delta T_f = 1.73 \dfrac{\text{mol}}{\text{kg}} \times 1.86 \dfrac{°C \cdot kg}{\text{mol}} = 3.22°C$

Freezing Point= $0.00 - 3.22 = -3.22°C$

$\Delta T_b = 1.73 \dfrac{\text{mol}}{\text{kg}} \times 0.512 \dfrac{°C \cdot kg}{\text{mol}} = 0.886°C$

Boiling Point=$100.000+0.886=100.886°C$

109. $0.2500 \text{ L C}_6H_{12}O_6 \times \dfrac{5.00 \text{ mol}}{1 \text{ L}} \times \dfrac{1}{1.40 \times 10^3 \text{ mL}} \times \dfrac{1 \text{ mL}}{1.06 \text{ g}} \times \dfrac{1000 \text{ g}}{1 \text{ kg}} = 0.84 \text{ m}$

$\Delta T_f = 0.84 \dfrac{\text{mol}}{\text{kg}} \times 1.86 \dfrac{°C \cdot kg}{\text{mol}} = 1.6°C$

Freezing Point= $0.0 - 1.6 = -1.6°C$

$\Delta T_b = 0.84 \dfrac{\text{mol}}{\text{kg}} \times 0.512 \dfrac{°C \cdot kg}{\text{mol}} = 0.43°C$

Boiling Point=$100.000+0.43=100.43°C$

Highlight Problems

111.   a) left to right
       b) right to left
       c) no movement

113. $0.100 \text{ g Hg} \times \dfrac{1 \text{ L}}{0.004 \text{ mg}} \times \dfrac{1000 \text{ mg}}{1 \text{ g}} = 3 x 10^4 \text{ L}$

Acids and Bases

14

Questions

1. The sour taste is due to the presence of acids in the candy, specifically citric acid and tartaric acid.

3. The properties of acids are:
   1) sour taste
   2) the ability to dissolve many metals
   3) turn litmus paper red

5. Organic acids contain the carboxylic acid group of atoms. Two examples of organic acids are citric acid and acetic acid.

7. Alkaloids are organic bases found in plants that are often poisonous.

9. An Arrhenius acid produces H^+ ions in aqueous solutions.
   $HCl\ (aq) \rightarrow H^+(aq) + Cl^-(aq)$

11. A Brønsted-Lowry acid is a proton (H^+) donor. A Brønsted-Lowry base is a proton acceptor. $HCl(aq) + H_2O(l) \rightarrow H_3O^+(aq) + Cl^-(aq)$

13. An acid-base neutralization reaction is when the hydrogen ion from the acid reacts with the hydroxide ion from the base to form water.
   $HCl\ (aq) + NaOH(aq) \rightarrow H_2O(l) + NaOH(aq)$

15. $2HCl(aq) + K_2O(s) \rightarrow H_2O(l) + 2KCl(aq)$

17. A titration is a laboratory procedure in which a reactant of known concentration is allowed to react with another compound of unknown concentration. The volumes of each solution are carefully monitored. The endpoint is the point during the experiment when an exact stoichiometric amount of each reactant has been added.

19. A strong acid will completely dissociate into component ions in solution to form a strong electrolyte. A weak acid will partially dissociate into component ions in solution to form a weak electrolyte.

21. A monoprotic acid contains only one hydrogen ion that will dissociate in solution. A diprotic acid contains two hydrogen ions that will dissociate in solution.

23. Yes, pure water contains H_3O^+ because of the process of self-ionization.

25. a) $[H_3O^+] > 1.0 \times 10^{-7}$ and $[OH^-] < 1.0 \times 10^{-7}$
    b) $[H_3O^+] < 1.0 \times 10^{-7}$ and $[OH^-] > 1.0 \times 10^{-7}$
    c) $[H_3O^+] = 1.0 \times 10^{-7}$ and $[OH^-] = 1.0 \times 10^{-7}$

27. A buffer is a solution that will resist a change in pH by reacting with either added acid or base.

29. The cause of acid rain is the combustion of fossil fuels.

31. Acid rain damages structures made out of metal, marble, cement, and limestone as well as causing harm and possible death to aquatic life and trees.

Problems

Acid and Base Definitions

33. a) acid: $HNO_3 (aq) \rightarrow H^+(aq) + NO_3^-(aq)$
    b) base: $KOH(aq) \rightarrow K^+(aq) + OH^-(aq)$
    c) acid: $HC_2H_3O_2 (aq) \rightarrow H^+(aq) + C_2H_3O_2^-(aq)$

35.

B-L Acid	B-L Base	Conj. Acid	Conj. Base
a) HBr	H_2O	H_3O^+	Br^-
b) H_2O	NH_3	NH_4^+	OH^-
c) HNO_3	H_2O	H_3O^+	NO_3^-
d) H_2O	C_5H_5N	$C_5H_5NH^+$	OH^-

37. a) conjugate acid-base pairs
    b) not conjugate acid-base pairs
    c) conjugate acid-base pairs
    d) not conjugate acid-base pairs

39. a) Cl^-
    b) HSO_3^-
    c) CHO_2^-
    d) F^-

41. a) NH_4^+
    b) $HClO_4$
    c) H_2SO_4
    d) HCO_3^-

Acid-Base Reactions

43. a) $HI(aq) + NaOH(aq) \rightarrow H_2O(l) + NaI(aq)$
    b) $HBr(aq) + KOH(aq) \rightarrow H_2O(l) + KBr(aq)$
    c) $2HNO_3(aq) + Ba(OH)_2(aq) \rightarrow 2H_2O(l) + Ba(NO_3)_2(aq)$
    d) $2HClO_4(aq) + Sr(OH)_2(aq) \rightarrow 2H_2O(l) + Sr(ClO_4)_2(aq)$

45. a) $2K(s) + 2HBr(aq) \rightarrow H_2(g) + 2KBr(aq)$
    b) $Ca(s) + 2HBr(aq) \rightarrow H_2(g) + CaBr_2(aq)$
    c) $Sr(s) + 2HBr(aq) \rightarrow H_2(g) + SrBr_2(aq)$
    d) $2Rb(s) + 2HBr(aq) \rightarrow H_2(g) + 2RbBr(aq)$

47. a) $MgO(s) + 2HI(aq) \rightarrow H_2O(l) + MgI_2(aq)$
    b) $K_2O(s) + 2HI(aq) \rightarrow H_2O(l) + 2KI(aq)$
    c) $Rb_2O(s) + 2HI(aq) \rightarrow H_2O(l) + 2RbI(aq)$
    d) $CaO(s) + 2HI(aq) \rightarrow H_2O(l) + CaI_2(aq)$

Acid-Base Titrations

49. $HCl(aq) + NaOH(aq) \rightarrow H_2O(l) + NaCl(aq)$

a) $0.02844 \text{ L NaOH} \times \dfrac{0.1231 \text{ mol NaOH}}{1 \text{ L}} \times \dfrac{1 \text{ mol HCl}}{1 \text{ mol NaOH}} \times \dfrac{1}{0.02500 \text{ L HCl}} =$

0.1400 M HCl

b) $0.02122 \text{ L NaOH} \times \dfrac{0.0972 \text{ mol NaOH}}{1 \text{ L}} \times \dfrac{1 \text{ mol HCl}}{1 \text{ mol NaOH}} \times \dfrac{1}{0.01500 \text{ L HCl}} =$

0.138 M HCl

c) $0.01488 \text{ L NaOH} \times \dfrac{0.1178 \text{ mol NaOH}}{1 \text{ L}} \times \dfrac{1 \text{ mol HCl}}{1 \text{ mol NaOH}} \times \dfrac{1}{0.02000 \text{ L HCl}} =$

0.08764 M HCl

d) $0.00688 \text{ L NaOH} \times \dfrac{0.1325 \text{ mol NaOH}}{1 \text{ L}} \times \dfrac{1 \text{ mol HCl}}{1 \text{ mol NaOH}} \times \dfrac{1}{0.00500 \text{ L HCl}} =$

0.182 M HCl

51. $H_2SO_4(aq) + 2KOH(aq) \rightarrow 2H_2O(l) + K_2SO_4(aq)$

$0.03833 \text{ L KOH} \times \dfrac{0.1328 \text{ mol KOH}}{1 \text{ L}} \times \dfrac{1 \text{ mol H}_2\text{SO}_4}{2 \text{ mol KOH}} \times \dfrac{1}{0.02500 \text{ L H}_2\text{SO}_4} =$

$0.1018 \text{ M H}_2\text{SO}_4$

Strong and Weak Acids and Bases

53. a) strong
    b) weak
    c) strong
    d) weak

55. a) $[H_3O^+] = 2.5$ M
    b) $[H_3O^+] = 1.2$ M
    c) $[H_3O^+] < 0.25$ M
    d) $[H_3O^+] < 2.25$ M

57. a) strong
    b) weak
    c) strong
    d) weak

59. a) $[OH^-] = 0.88$ M
    b) $[OH^-] < 0.88$ M
    c) $[OH^-] = 0.88$ M
    d) $[OH^-] = 1.55$ M

Acidity, Basicity, and K_w

61. a) acidic
    b) acidic
    c) neutral
    d) basic

63. a) $K_w = [H_3O^+][OH^-] \Rightarrow [OH^-] = \dfrac{K_w}{[H_3O^+]} = \dfrac{1.0 \times 10^{-14}}{1.5 \times 10^{-9}} = 6.7 \times 10^{-6}$ M, Basic

    b) $K_w = [H_3O^+][OH^-] \Rightarrow [OH^-] = \dfrac{K_w}{[H_3O^+]} = \dfrac{1.0 \times 10^{-14}}{9.3 \times 10^{-9}} = 1.1 \times 10^{-6}$ M, Basic

    c) $K_w = [H_3O^+][OH^-] \Rightarrow [OH^-] = \dfrac{K_w}{[H_3O^+]} = \dfrac{1.0 \times 10^{-14}}{2.2 \times 10^{-6}} = 4.5 \times 10^{-9}$ M, Acidic

    d) $K_w = [H_3O^+][OH^-] \Rightarrow [OH^-] = \dfrac{K_w}{[H_3O^+]} = \dfrac{1.0 \times 10^{-14}}{7.4 \times 10^{-4}} = 1.4 \times 10^{-11}$ M, Acidic

65. a) $K_w = [H_3O^+][OH^-] \Rightarrow [H_3O^+] = \dfrac{K_w}{[OH^-]} = \dfrac{1.0 \times 10^{-14}}{2.7 \times 10^{-12}} = 3.7 \times 10^{-3} \text{M, Acidic}$

b) $K_w = [H_3O^+][OH^-] \Rightarrow [H_3O^+] = \dfrac{K_w}{[OH^-]} = \dfrac{1.0 \times 10^{-14}}{2.5 \times 10^{-2}} = 4.0 \times 10^{-13} \text{M, Basic}$

c) $K_w = [H_3O^+][OH^-] \Rightarrow [H_3O^+] = \dfrac{K_w}{[OH^-]} = \dfrac{1.0 \times 10^{-14}}{1.1 \times 10^{-10}} = 9.1 \times 10^{-5} \text{M, Acidic}$

d) $K_w = [H_3O^+][OH^-] \Rightarrow [H_3O^+] = \dfrac{K_w}{[OH^-]} = \dfrac{1.0 \times 10^{-14}}{3.3 \times 10^{-4}} = 3.0 \times 10^{-11} \text{M, Basic}$

pH

67. a) basic
b) neutral
c) acidic
d) acidic

69. a) $pH = -\log[H^+] = -\log[1.7 \times 10^{-8}] = 7.77$

b) $pH = -\log[H^+] = -\log[1.0 \times 10^{-7}] = 7.00$

c) $pH = -\log[H^+] = -\log[2.2 \times 10^{-6}] = 5.66$

d) $pH = -\log[H^+] = -\log[7.4 \times 10^{-4}] = 3.13$

71. a) $[H_3O^+] = 10^{-pH} = 10^{-8.55} = 2.8 \times 10^{-9} \text{M}$

b) $[H_3O^+] = 10^{-pH} = 10^{-11.23} = 5.9 \times 10^{-12} \text{M}$

c) $[H_3O^+] = 10^{-pH} = 10^{-2.87} = 1.3 \times 10^{-3} \text{M}$

d) $[H_3O^+] = 10^{-pH} = 10^{-1.22} = 6.0 \times 10^{-2} \text{M}$

73. a) $[H_3O^+] = \dfrac{K_w}{[OH^-]} = \dfrac{1.0 \times 10^{-14}}{1.9 \times 10^{-7}} = 5.3 \times 10^{-8} \text{M}, \ pH = -\log 5.3 \times 10^{-8} = 7.28$

b) $[H_3O^+] = \dfrac{K_w}{[OH^-]} = \dfrac{1.0 \times 10^{-14}}{2.6 \times 10^{-8}} = 3.8 \times 10^{-7} \text{M}, \ pH = -\log 3.8 \times 10^{-7} = 6.41$

73. (cont.)

c) $[H_3O^+] = \dfrac{K_w}{[OH^-]} = \dfrac{1.0 \times 10^{-14}}{7.2 \times 10^{-11}} = 1.4 \times 10^{-4}$ M, pH $= -\log 1.4 \times 10^{-4} = 3.86$

d) $[H_3O^+] = \dfrac{K_w}{[OH^-]} = \dfrac{1.0 \times 10^{-14}}{9.5 \times 10^{-2}} = 1.1 \times 10^{-13}$ M, pH $= -\log 1.1 \times 10^{-13} = 12.96$

75. a) $[H_3O^+] = 10^{-pH} = 10^{-4.25} = 5.6 \times 10^{-5}$ M, $[OH^-] = \dfrac{K_w}{[H_3O^+]} = \dfrac{1.0 \times 10^{-14}}{5.6 \times 10^{-5}} = 1.8 \times 10^{-10}$ M

b) $[H_3O^+] = 10^{-pH} = 10^{-12.53} = 3.0 \times 10^{-13}$ M, $[OH^-] = \dfrac{K_w}{[H_3O^+]} = \dfrac{1.0 \times 10^{-14}}{3.0 \times 10^{-13}} = 3.3 \times 10^{-2}$ M

c) $[H_3O^+] = 10^{-pH} = 10^{-1.50} = 3.2 \times 10^{-2}$ M, $[OH^-] = \dfrac{K_w}{[H_3O^+]} = \dfrac{1.0 \times 10^{-14}}{3.2 \times 10^{-2}} = 3.1 \times 10^{-13}$ M

d) $[H_3O^+] = 10^{-pH} = 10^{-8.25} = 5.6 \times 10^{-9}$ M, $[OH^-] = \dfrac{K_w}{[H_3O^+]} = \dfrac{1.0 \times 10^{-14}}{5.6 \times 10^{-9}} = 1.8 \times 10^{-6}$ M

Buffers and Acid Rain

77. Correct answers vary.

79. a) not a buffer
b) not a buffer
c) buffer
d) buffer

81. c) $NaF(aq) + HCl(aq) \rightarrow HF(aq) + NaCl(aq)$
d) $KC_2H_3O_2(aq) + HCl(aq) \rightarrow HC_2H_3O_2(aq) + KCl(aq)$

Cumulative Exercises

83. $HCl(aq) + NaOH(aq) \rightarrow H_2O(l) + NaCl(aq)$

$\dfrac{0.250 \text{ mol NaOH}}{1 \text{ L}} \times 0.0200 \text{ L} \times \dfrac{1 \text{ mol HCl}}{1 \text{ mol NaOH}} \times \dfrac{1 \text{ L}}{0.100 \text{ mol HCl}} = 0.0500 \text{ L}$

85. $Mg(s) + 2HCl(aq) \rightarrow H_2(g) + CaCl_2(aq)$

$10.0 \text{ g Mg} \times \dfrac{1 \text{ mol Mg}}{24.31 \text{ g}} \times \dfrac{2 \text{ mol HCl}}{1 \text{ mol Mg}} \times \dfrac{1 \text{ L}}{5.0 \text{ mol HCl}} = 0.16 \text{ L}$

87. $K_2O(s) + 2HI(aq) \rightarrow H_2O(l) + 2KI(aq)$

$$18.5 \text{ g } K_2O \times \frac{1 \text{ mol } K_2O}{94.20 \text{ g}} \times \frac{2 \text{ mol } KI}{1 \text{ mol } K_2O} \times \frac{166.0 \text{ g}}{1 \text{ mol } KI} = 65.2 \text{ g } KI$$

88. $HX(aq) + NaOH(aq) \rightarrow H_2O(l) + NaX(aq)$

$$\frac{0.1003 \text{ mol } NaOH}{1 \text{ L}} \times 0.02077 \text{ L} \times \frac{1 \text{ mol } HX}{1 \text{ mol } NaOH} = 2.083 x 10^{-3} \text{ mol}$$

$$\text{molar mass} = \frac{0.125 \text{ g}}{2.083 x 10^{-3} \text{ mol}} = 60.0 \text{ g/mol}$$

89. a) pH = -log 0.0025 = 2.60; acidic
    b) pH = -log $1.8 x 10^{-12}$ = 11.74; basic
    c) pH = -log $9.6 x 10^{-9}$ = 8.02; basic
    d) pH = -log 0.0195 = 1.71; acidic

93.

$[H_3O^+]$	$[OH^-]$	pH	acidic or basic
$1.0 x 10^{-4}$	$1.0 x 10^{-10}$	4.00	acidic
$5.5 x 10^{-3}$	$1.8 x 10^{-12}$	2.26	acidic
$3.1 x 10^{-9}$	$3.2 x 10^{-6}$	8.50	basic
$4.8 x 10^{-9}$	$2.1 x 10^{-6}$	8.32	basic
$2.8 x 10^{-8}$	$3.5 x 10^{-7}$	7.55	basic

95.

	$[H_3O^+]$	$[OH^-]$	pH
a)	[0.0150]	$\frac{1.00 x 10^{-14}}{0.0150} = 6.67 x 10^{-13}$	1.823
b)	$[1.5 x 10^{-3}]$	$\frac{1.00 x 10^{-14}}{1.5 x 10^{-3}} = 6.7 x 10^{-12}$	2.82
c)	$[9.77 x 10^{-4}]$	$\frac{1.00 x 10^{-14}}{9.77 x 10^{-4}} = 1.02 x 10^{-11}$	3.010
d)	[0.0878]	$\frac{1.00 x 10^{-14}}{0.0878} = 1.14 x 10^{-13}$	1.057

97.

[H$_3$O$^+$]	[OH$^-$]	pH
a) $\dfrac{1.00x10^{-14}}{0.15} = 6.7x10^{-14}$	[0.15]	13.17
b) $\dfrac{1.00x10^{-14}}{3.0x10^{-3}} = 3.3x10^{-12}$	[3.0x10^{-3}]	11.48
c) $\dfrac{1.00x10^{-14}}{9.6x10^{-4}} = 1.0x10^{-11}$	[9.6x10^{-4}]	11.00
d) $\dfrac{1.00x10^{-14}}{8.7x10^{-5}} = 1.1x10^{-10}$	[8.7x10^{-5}]	9.96

Highlight Problems

99. a) weak
    b) strong
    c) weak
    d) strong

101. Great Lakes: pH = 4.5 $\Rightarrow$ [H$^+$]=10$^{-4.5}$=3.2x10^{-5}M

West Coast: pH = 5.4 $\Rightarrow$ [H$^+$]=10$^{-5.4}$=4.0x10^{-6}M

Ratio: $\dfrac{3.2x10^{-5}}{4.0x10^{-6}}$ = 8 times more concentrated

Chemical Equilibrium

15

Questions

1. The two general concepts involved in equilibrium are sameness and changelessness.

3. The rate of a chemical reaction is the amount of reactant that changes to product in a given period of time.

5. Chemists seek to control reaction rates so that a desired result is obtained. The goal may be to prevent a reaction from going too fast and becoming dangerous, or it may be to speed it up so that it proceeds at a fast enough rate to be used in industrial settings.

7. The two factors that influence reaction rates are concentration and temperature. The rate of a reaction increases with increasing concentration. The rate of a reaction increases with increasing temperature.

9. Dynamic equilibrium exists when the rate of the forward reaction is equal to the rate of the reverse reaction.

11. Because the rate of the forward and reverse reactions is the same at equilibrium, the relative concentrations of reactants and products becomes constant. It doesn't matter if it is a high or a low concentration, it simply remains constant.

13. The equilibrium constant is a measure of how far a reaction goes. It is significant because it is used to quantify the concentration of all compounds in a reaction at equilibrium.

15. A small equilibrium constant characterizes a system that will have high concentrations of reactants and low concentrations of products at equilibrium. A large equilibrium constant characterizes a system that will have low concentrations of reactants and high concentrations of products at equilibrium.

17. No, the concentrations of reactants and products will not always be the same in every equilibrium mixture of a particular reaction at a given temperature. The final concentrations will depend on the initial concentrations and will adjust accordingly so that the K_{eq} value is achieved.

19. Correct answers may vary.

21. The reaction will proceed in the reverse (left) direction.

23. The reaction will proceed in the forward (right) direction.

25. The reaction will proceed in the forward (right) direction.

27. The reaction will proceed in the forward (right) direction.

29. The reaction will proceed in the reverse (left) direction if you increase the temperature of an exothermic reaction at equilibrium. The reaction will proceed in the forward (right) direction if you decrease the temperature of an exothermic reaction at equilibrium.

31. $K_{sp} = [A^{+2}][B^-]^2$

33. Solubility is the amount of a compound that dissolves in a specified amount of liquid. The molar solubility is just the solubility expressed in molarity.

35. Two reactants with a large K_{eq} may not react immediately when combined because there may be a large activation energy barrier that the reactants must overcome in order for the reaction to occur.

37. The catalyst does NOT affect the value of the equilibrium constant: it merely allows the reaction to reach equilibrium faster than without a catalyst.

Problems

The Equilibrium Constant

39. a) $K_{eq} = \dfrac{[N_2O_4]}{[NO_2]^2}$

b) $K_{eq} = \dfrac{[NO]^2[Br_2]}{[BrNO]^2}$

c) $K_{eq} = \dfrac{[H_2][CO_2]}{[H_2O][CO]}$

d) $K_{eq} = \dfrac{[CS_2][H_2]^4}{[CH_4][H_2S]^2}$

41. a) $K_{eq} = \dfrac{[Cl_2]}{[PCl_5]}$

b) $K_{eq} = [O_2]^3$

c) $K_{eq} = \dfrac{[H_3O^+][F^-]}{[HF]}$

d) $K_{eq} = \dfrac{[NH_4^+][OH^-]}{[NH_3]}$

43. $K_{eq} = \dfrac{[H_2]^2[S_2]}{[H_2S]^2}$

45. a) reactants
    b) products
    c) reactants
    d) both

Calculating and Using Equilibrium Constants

47. $K_{eq} = \dfrac{[0.105][0.0844]}{[0.225]} = 0.0394$

49. $K_{eq} = \dfrac{[2.74x10^{-2}]^2[7.54x10^{-3}]}{[0.562]^2} = 1.79x10^{-5}$

51. $K_{eq} = [0.278][0.355] = 0.0987$

53. $K_{eq} = \dfrac{[0.0357][0.0112]}{[SbCl_5]} = 4.9x10^{-4} \Rightarrow [SbCl_5] = \dfrac{[0.0357][0.0112]}{4.9x10^{-4}} = 0.82$

55. $K_{eq} = \dfrac{[ICl]^2}{[0.0112][0.0155]} = 81.9 \Rightarrow [ICl] = \sqrt{(81.9)[0.0112][0.0155]} = 0.119$

57. T(K)	$[N_2]$	$[H_2]$	$[NH_3]$	K_{eq}
500	0.115	0.105	0.439	$1.45x10^3$
575	0.110	0.24	0.128	9.6
775	0.120	0.140	$4.39x10^{-3}$	0.0584

Le Châtelier's Principle

59. a) shift right
    b) shift left
    c) shift right

61. a) unchanged
    b) shift left
    c) shift left
    d) shift right

63. a) shift right
    b) shift left

65. a) no effect
    b) no effect

67. a) shift right
    b) shift left

69. a) shift left
    b) shift right

71. a) no effect
    b) shift right
    c) shift left
    d) shift right
    e) no effect

The Solubility-Product Constant

73. a) $CaSO_4 \rightleftarrows Ca^{+2}(aq) + SO_4^{-2}(aq); \quad K_{sp}=[Ca^{+2}][SO_4^{-2}]$

b) $AgCl \rightleftarrows Ag^+(aq) + Cl^-(aq); \quad K_{sp}=[Ag^+][Cl^-]$

c) $CuS \rightleftarrows Cu^{+2}(aq) + S^{-2}(aq); \quad K_{sp}=[Cu^{+2}][S^{-2}]$

d) $FeCO_3 \rightleftarrows Fe^{+2}(aq) + CO_3^{-2}(aq); \quad K_{sp}=[Fe^{+2}][CO_3^{-2}]$

75. $K_{sp}=[Fe^{+2}][OH^-]^2$

77. $K_{sp}=[2.6x10^{-4}][5.2x10^{-4}]^2 = 7.0x10^{-11}$

79. $K_{sp}=[Pb^{+2}][SO_4^{-2}] \Rightarrow [SO_4^{-2}] = \dfrac{K_{sp}}{[Pb^{+2}]} = \dfrac{1.82x10^{-8}}{1.35x10^{-4}} = 1.35x10^{-4}$

81. $[Ca^{+2}]=[CO_3^{-2}] = S \Rightarrow K_{sp} = S^2 \Rightarrow S = \sqrt{4.96x10^{-9}} = [7.04x10^{-5}]$

83. $[Mg^{+2}]=[CO_3^{-2}] = S \Rightarrow K_{sp} = S^2 \Rightarrow S = \sqrt{6.82x10^{-6}} = [2.61x10^{-3}]$

85.

Compound	[Cation]	[Anion]	K_{sp}
$SrCO_3$	$2.4x10^{-5}$	$2.4x10^{-5}$	$\underline{5.8x10^{-10}}$
SrF_2	$1.0x10^{-3}$	$\underline{2.0x10^{-3}}$	$4.0x10^{-9}$
Ag_2CO_3	$\underline{2.6x10^{-4}}$	$1.3x10^{-4}$	$8.8x10^{-12}$

87. $Fe^{+3}_{equilibrium} = Fe^{+3}_{initial} - Fe^{+3}_{reacted}$

$$\frac{1.7x10^{-4} \text{ mol FeSCN}^{+2}}{L} \times \frac{1 \text{ mol Fe}^{+3}}{1 \text{ mol FeSCN}^{+2}} = 1.7x10^{-4} \text{ M Fe}^{+2}$$

$$[Fe^{+3}] = 1.0x10^{-3} - 1.7x10^{-4} = 8.3x10^{-4}$$

$$SCN^{-}_{equilibrium} = SCN^{-}_{initial} - SCN^{-}_{reacted}$$

$$\frac{1.7x10^{-4} \text{ mol FeSCN}^{+2}}{L} \times \frac{1 \text{ mol SCN}^{-}}{1 \text{ mol FeSCN}^{+2}} = 1.7x10^{-4} \text{ M SCN}^{-}$$

$$[SCN^{-}] = 8.0x10^{-4} - 1.7x10^{-4} = 6.3x10^{-4}$$

$$K_{eq} = \frac{[FeSCN^{+2}]}{[Fe^{+3}][SCN^{-}]} = \frac{[1.7x10^{-4}]}{[8.3x10^{-4}][6.3x10^{-4}]} = 3.3x10^{2}$$

89. $K_{eq} = \frac{[HI]^2}{[H_2][I_2]} \Rightarrow 6.17x10^2 = \frac{[HI]^2}{[0.104][0.0202]} \Rightarrow$

$$[HI] = \sqrt{(6.17x10^2)[0.104][0.0202]} = 1.14 \text{ M}$$

$$\frac{1.14 \text{ mol HI}}{1 \text{ L}} \times 3.67 \text{ L} \times \frac{127.91 \text{ g}}{1 \text{ mol HI}} = 535 \text{ g HI}$$

91. a) no
    b) yes
    c) yes
    d) yes

93. $[Cu^{+2}] = [S^{-2}] = S \Rightarrow K_{sp} = S^2 \Rightarrow S = \sqrt{1.27x10^{-36}} = [1.13x10^{-18}]$

$$\frac{1.13x10^{-18} \text{ mol CuS}}{1 \text{ L}} \times 5.0\text{L} \times \frac{95.62 \text{ g}}{1 \text{ mol CuS}} = 5.4x10^{-16}\text{g}$$

95. Equilibrium was reached at figure e.

97. $[Ca^{+2}]=[CO_3^{-2}] = S \Rightarrow K_{sp} = S^2 \Rightarrow S = \sqrt{4.96 x 10^{-9}} = [7.04 x 10^{-5}]$

$$0.250 \text{ g CaCO}_3 \times \frac{1 \text{ mol CaCO}_3}{100.09 \text{ g}} \times \frac{1 \text{ L}}{7.04 x 10^{-5} \text{ mol}} = 35.5 \text{ L}$$

Oxidation and Reduction

16

Questions

1. The fuel-cell electric vehicle is an automobile that has an electric motor powered by the reaction between hydrogen and oxygen.

3. a) Oxidation is when a substance gains oxygen atoms in the reaction. Reduction is when oxygen is lost from a substance.
   b) Oxidation is when a substance loses electrons. Reduction is when a substance gains electrons.
   c) Oxidation is an increase in the oxidation state of a substance. Reduction is a decrease in the oxidation state of a substance.

5. A reducing agent is the substance being oxidized.

7. Good reducing agents have a strong tendency to <u>lose</u> electrons in reactions.

9. The oxidation state of a monatomic ion is equal to the charge of the ion.

11. For an ion, the sum of the oxidation states of the individual atoms must sum to <u>the ion charge</u>.

13. In a redox reaction, an atom that undergoes an increase in oxidation state is <u>oxidized</u>. An atom that undergoes a decrease in oxidation state is <u>reduced</u>.

15. When balancing redox equations, the number of electrons lost in the oxidation half-reaction must <u>equal</u> the number of electrons gained in the reduction half-reaction.

17. When balancing aqueous redox reactions occurring in acidic media, hydrogen is balanced using <u>hydrogen ions</u>.

19. The metals at the top of the activity series are the most reactive.

21. The metals at the bottom of the activity series are least likely to lose electrons.

23. Metals above H_2 on the activity series will dissolve in acids, while metals below H_2 will not dissolve in acids.

25. Oxidation occurs at the <u>anode</u> of an electrochemical cell.

27. The role of a salt bridge is to allow for the flow of ions between two halves of an electrochemical cell, which completes the electrical circuit.

29. The common dry cell battery contains only a small amount of liquid water within it, hence the name. The cell voltage is approximately 1.5 volts.
The anode reaction: $Zn(s) \rightarrow Zn^{+2}(aq) + 2e^-$.
The cathode reaction: $2MnO_2(s) + 2NH_4^+(aq) + 2e^- \rightarrow Mn_2O_3(s) + 2 NH_3(g) + H_2O(l)$.

31. A fuel cell operates much like a battery, however the reactants in a fuel cell are continually replenished from an external supply as the reaction proceeds. The most common fuel cell is the hydrogen-oxygen fuel cell. The reaction at the anode is the oxidation of hydrogen gas to form water according to the half-reaction: $H_2(g) + 4OH^-(aq) \rightarrow 4H_2O(l) + 4e^-$. The reaction at the cathode corresponds to the reduction of oxygen gas to form hydroxide ion according to the half-reaction, $O_2(g) + 2H_2O(l) + 4e^- \rightarrow 4OH^-$.

33. The oxidation of metals to form a metal oxide is called corrosion. For the corrosion of iron: The oxidation half-reaction is $2Fe(s) \rightarrow 2 Fe^{+2}(aq) + 4e^-$. The reduction half-reaction is $O_2(g) + 2H_2O(l) + 4e^- \rightarrow 4 OH^-(aq)$.

Problems

Oxidation and Reduction

35. a) H_2
    b) Al
    c) Al

37.

	Oxidized	Reduced
a)	Sr	O_2
b)	Ca	Cl_2
c)	Mg	Ni^{+2}

39.

	Oxidizing Agent	Reducing Agent
a)	O_2	Sr
b)	Cl_2	Ca
c)	Ni^{+2}	Mg

41. a) no
    b) yes
    c) no
    d) yes

43. a) yes
    b) no
    c) yes
    d) no

45.

	Oxidized	Reduced	Oxidizing Agent	Reducing Agent
a)	N_2	O_2	O_2	N_2
b)	C in CO	O_2	O_2	C in CO
c)	Cl in $SbCl_5$	Sb in $SbCl_5$	Sb in $SbCl_5$	Cl in $SbCl_5$
d)	K	Pb^{+2}	Pb^{+2}	K

Oxidation States

47. a) 0
    b) +2
    c) 0
    d) 0

49. a) Na=+1, Cl=$^-$1
    b) Ca=+2, F=$^-$1
    c) S=+4, O=$^-$2
    d) H=+1, S=$^-$2

51. a) +2
    b) +4
    c) +1

53. a) C=+4, O=$^-$2
    b) O=$^-$2, H=+1
    c) N=+5, O=$^-$2
    d) N=+3, O=$^-$2

55. a) +1
    b) +3
    c) +5
    d) +7

57. a) Sb: +5 → +3, reduced; Cl: $^-$1→ 0, oxidized
    b) C: +2 → +4, oxidized; Cl: 0 → $^-$1, reduced; O: $^-$2 → $^-$2, neither
    c) N: +2 → +3, oxidized; O: $^-$2 → $^-$2, neither; Br: 0 → $^-$1, reduced
    d) H: 0 → +1, oxidized; C: +4 → +2, reduced; O: $^-$2 → $^-$2, neither

59. Na: $0 \rightarrow +1$, reducing agent; H: $+1 \rightarrow 0$, oxidizing agent; O: $^-2 \rightarrow {}^-2$, neither

Balancing Redox Reactions

61. a) 1: $\underset{0}{K}(s) + \underset{+3}{Cr^{+3}}(aq) \rightarrow \underset{0}{Cr}(s) + \underset{+1}{K^+}(aq)$

   2: $K(s) \rightarrow K^+(aq)$ $\qquad\qquad Cr^{+3}(aq) \rightarrow Cr(s)$

   3: $K(s) \rightarrow K^+(aq)$ $\qquad\qquad Cr^{+3}(aq) \rightarrow Cr(s)$

   4: $K(s) \rightarrow K^+(aq) + 1e^-$ $\qquad Cr^{+3}(aq) + 3e^- \rightarrow Cr(s)$

   5: $3K(s) \rightarrow 3K^+(aq) + 3e^-$ $\quad Cr^{+3}(aq) + 3e^- \rightarrow Cr(s)$

   6: Overall: $3K(s) + Cr^{+3}(aq) \rightarrow 3K^+(aq) + Cr(s)$

   b) 1: $\underset{0}{Mg}(s) + \underset{+1}{Ag^+}(aq) \rightarrow \underset{+2}{Mg^{+2}}(aq) + \underset{0}{Ag}(s)$

   2: $Mg(s) \rightarrow Mg^{+2}(aq)$ $\qquad Ag^+(aq) \rightarrow Ag(s)$

   3: $Mg(s) \rightarrow Mg^{+2}(aq)$ $\qquad Ag^+(aq) \rightarrow Ag(s)$

   4: $Mg(s) \rightarrow Mg^{+2}(aq) + 2e^-$ $\quad Ag^+(aq) + 1e^- \rightarrow Ag(s)$

   5: $Mg(s) \rightarrow Mg^{+2}(aq) + 2e^-$ $\quad 2Ag^+(aq) + 2e^- \rightarrow 2Ag(s)$

   6: Overall: $Mg(s) + 2Ag^+(aq) \rightarrow Mg^{+2}(aq) + 2Ag(s)$

   c) 1: $\underset{0}{Al}(s) + \underset{+2}{Fe^{+2}}(aq) \rightarrow \underset{+3}{Al^{+3}}(aq) + \underset{0}{Fe}(s)$

   2: $Al(s) \rightarrow Al^{+3}(aq)$ $\qquad\qquad Fe^{+2}(aq) \rightarrow Fe(s)$

   3: $Al(s) \rightarrow Al^{+3}(aq)$ $\qquad\qquad Fe^{+2}(aq) \rightarrow Fe(s)$

   4: $Al(s) \rightarrow Al^{+3}(aq) + 3e^-$ $\qquad Fe^{+2}(aq) + 2e^- \rightarrow Fe(s)$

   5: $2Al(s) \rightarrow 2Al^{+3}(aq) + 6e^-$ $\quad 3Fe^{+2}(aq) + 6e^- \rightarrow 3Fe(s)$

   6: Overall: $2Al(s) + 3Fe^{+2}(aq) \rightarrow 2Al^{+3}(aq) + 3Fe(s)$

63. a) 1: $\underset{+7}{MnO_4^-}(aq) \rightarrow \underset{+2}{Mn^{+2}}(aq)$ reduction

   2: $MnO_4^-(aq) \rightarrow Mn^{+2}(aq)$

   3: $MnO_4^-(aq) + 8H^+(aq) \rightarrow Mn^{+2}(aq) + 4H_2O(l)$

   4: $MnO_4^-(aq) + 8H^+(aq) + 5e^- \rightarrow Mn^{+2}(aq) + 4H_2O(l)$

b) 1: $\underset{+2}{Pb^{+2}}(aq) \rightarrow \underset{+4}{PbO_2}(s)$ oxidation

   2: $Pb^{+2}(aq) \rightarrow PbO_2(s)$

   3: $Pb^{+2}(aq) + 2H_2O(l) \rightarrow PbO_2(s) + 4H^+(aq)$

   4: $Pb^{+2}(aq) + 2H_2O(l) \rightarrow PbO_2(s) + 4H^+(aq) + 2e^-$

c) 1: $\underset{+5}{IO_3^-}(aq) \rightarrow \underset{0}{I_2}(s)$ reduction

   2: $IO_3^-(aq) \rightarrow I_2(s)$

   3: $2IO_3^-(aq) + 12H^+(aq) \rightarrow I_2(s) + 6H_2O(l)$

   4: $2IO_3^-(aq) + 12H^+(aq) + 10e^- \rightarrow I_2(s) + 6H_2O(l)$

d) 1: $\underset{+4}{SO_2}(g) \rightarrow \underset{+6}{SO_4^{-2}}(aq)$ oxidation

   2: $SO_2(g) \rightarrow SO_4^{-2}(aq)$

   3: $SO_2(g) + 2H_2O(l) \rightarrow SO_4^{-2}(aq) + 4H^+(aq)$

   4: $SO_2(g) + 2H_2O(l) \rightarrow SO_4^{-2}(aq) + 4H^+(aq) + 2e^-$

65. a) 1: $\underset{+4}{PbO_2(s)} + \underset{-1}{I^-(aq)} \rightarrow \underset{+2}{Pb^{+2}(aq)} + \underset{0}{I_2(s)}$

2: $PbO_2 \rightarrow Pb^{+2}$ $\qquad\qquad\qquad$ $I^- \rightarrow I_2$

3: $PbO_2 + 4H^+ \rightarrow Pb^{+2} + 2H_2O$ $\qquad$ $2I^- \rightarrow I_2$

4: $PbO_2 + 4H^+ + 2e^- \rightarrow Pb^{+2} + 2H_2O$ $\qquad$ $2I^- \rightarrow I_2 + 1e^-$

5: $PbO_2 + 4H^+ + 2e^- \rightarrow Pb^{+2} + 2H_2O$ $\qquad$ $4I^- \rightarrow 2I_2 + 2e^-$

6: $PbO_2(s) + 4H^+(aq) + 4I^-(aq) \rightarrow Pb^{+2}(aq) + 2H_2O(l) + 2I_2(s)$

b) 1: $\underset{+4}{SO_3^{-2}(aq)} + \underset{+7}{MnO_4^-(aq)} \rightarrow \underset{+6}{SO_4^{-2}(aq)} + \underset{+2}{Mn^{+2}(s)}$

2: $SO_3^{-2} \rightarrow SO_4^{-2}$ $\qquad\qquad\qquad$ $MnO_4^- \rightarrow Mn^{+2}$

3: $SO_3^{-2} + H_2O \rightarrow SO_4^{-2} + 2H^+$ $\qquad$ $MnO_4^- + 8H^+ \rightarrow Mn^{+2} + 4H_2O$

4: $SO_3^{-2} + H_2O \rightarrow SO_4^{-2} + 2H^+ + 2e^-$ $\qquad$ $MnO_4^- + 8H^+ + 5e^- \rightarrow Mn^{+2} + 4H_2O$

5: $5SO_3^{-2} + 5H_2O \rightarrow 5SO_4^{-2} + 10H^+ + 10e^-$ $\quad$ $2MnO_4^- + 16H^+ + 10e^- \rightarrow 2Mn^{+2} + 8H_2O$

6: $5SO_3^{-2}(aq) + 2MnO_4^-(aq) + 6H^+(aq) \rightarrow 5SO_4^{-2}(aq) + 2Mn^{+2}(aq) + 3H_2O(l)$

c) 1: $\underset{+2}{S_2O_3^{-2}(aq)} + \underset{0}{Cl_2(g)} \rightarrow \underset{+6}{SO_4^{-2}(aq)} + \underset{-1}{Cl^-(aq)}$

2: $S_2O_3^{-2} \rightarrow SO_4^{-2}$ $\qquad\qquad\qquad$ $Cl_2 \rightarrow Cl^-$

3: $S_2O_3^{-2} + 5H_2O \rightarrow 2SO_4^{-2} + 10H^'$ $\qquad$ $Cl_2 \rightarrow 2Cl^-$

4: $S_2O_3^{-2} + 5H_2O \rightarrow 2SO_4^{-2} + 10H^+ + 8e^-$ $\qquad$ $Cl_2 + 2e^- \rightarrow 2Cl^-$

5: $S_2O_3^{-2} + 5H_2O \rightarrow 2SO_4^{-2} + 10H^+ + 8e^-$ $\qquad$ $4Cl_2 + 8e^- \rightarrow 8Cl^-$

6: $S_2O_3^{-2}(aq) + 5H_2O(l) + 4Cl_2(g) \rightarrow 2SO_4^{-2}(aq) + 10H^+(aq) + 8Cl^-(aq)$

67. a) 1: $\underset{+7}{ClO_4^-}(aq) + \underset{-1}{Cl^-}(aq) \rightarrow \underset{+5}{ClO_3^-}(aq) + \underset{0}{Cl_2}(g)$

    2: $ClO_4^- \rightarrow ClO_3^-$ $Cl^- \rightarrow Cl_2$

    3: $ClO_4^- + 2H^+ \rightarrow ClO_3^- + H_2O$ $2Cl^- \rightarrow Cl_2$

    4: $ClO_4^- + 2H^+ + 2e^- \rightarrow ClO_3^- + H_2O$ $2Cl^- \rightarrow Cl_2 + 2e^-$

    5: $ClO_4^- + 2H^+ + 2e^- \rightarrow ClO_3^- + H_2O$ $2Cl^- \rightarrow Cl_2 + 2e^-$

    6: $ClO_4^-(aq) + 2H^+(aq) + 2Cl^-(aq) \rightarrow ClO_3^-(aq) + H_2O(l) + Cl_2(g)$

b) 1: $\underset{+7}{MnO_4^-}(aq) + \underset{0}{Al}(s) \rightarrow \underset{+2}{Mn^{+2}}(aq) + \underset{+3}{Al^{+3}}(aq)$

    2: $MnO_4^- \rightarrow Mn^{+2}$ $Al \rightarrow Al^{+3}$

    3: $MnO_4^- + 8H^+ \rightarrow Mn^{+2} + 4H_2O$ $Al \rightarrow Al^{+3}$

    4: $MnO_4^- + 8H^+ + 5e^- \rightarrow Mn^{+2} + 4H_2O$ $Al \rightarrow Al^{+3} + 3e^-$

    5: $3MnO_4^- + 24H^+ + 15e^- \rightarrow 3Mn^{+2} + 12H_2O$ $5Al \rightarrow 5Al^{+3} + 15e^-$

    6: $3MnO_4^-(aq) + 24H^+(aq) + 5Al(s) \rightarrow 3Mn^{+2}(aq) + 12H_2O(l) + 5Al^{+3}(aq)$

c) 1: $\underset{0}{Br_2}(aq) + \underset{0}{Sn}(s) \rightarrow \underset{+2}{Sn^{+2}}(aq) + \underset{-1}{Br^-}(aq)$

    2: $Br_2 \rightarrow Br^-$ $Sn \rightarrow Sn^{+2}$

    3: $Br_2 \rightarrow 2Br^-$ $Sn \rightarrow Sn^{+2}$

    4: $Br_2 + 2e^- \rightarrow 2Br^-$ $Sn \rightarrow Sn^{+2} + 2e^-$

    5: $Br_2 + 2e^- \rightarrow 2Br^-$ $Sn \rightarrow Sn^{+2} + 2e^-$

    6: $Br_2(aq) + Sn(s) \rightarrow Sn^{+2}(aq) + 2Br^-(aq)$

The Activity Series

69. c) Pb

71. b) Cu^{+2}

73. b) Al

75. a) no reaction
    b) spontaneous
    c) spontaneous
    d) no reaction

77. You could use any of the following metals: Fe, Cr, Zn, Mn, Al, Mg, Na, Ca, K, Li.

79. Al will reduce Mn^{+2} but not Mg^{+2}.

81. a) $2Al + 6HCl \rightarrow 3H_2 + 2Al^{+3} + 6Cl^-$
    b) no reaction
    c) $Pb + 2 HCl \rightarrow Pb^{+2} + H_2 + 2Cl^-$
    d) $2Cr + 6HCl \rightarrow 3H_2 + 2Cr^{+3} + 6Cl^-$

Batteries, Electrochemical Cells, and Electrolysis

83. The electrochemical cell:

85. Choice d would produce the highest voltage.

87. The overall reaction for an alkaline battery is:

cathode: $2MnO_2(s) + 2H_2O(l) + 2e^- \rightarrow 2MnO(OH)(s) + 2OH^-(aq)$

+anode: $Zn(s) + 2OH^-(aq) \rightarrow Zn(OH)_2(s) + 2e^-$
_____

Overall: $2MnO_2(s) + 2H_2O(l) + Zn(s) \rightarrow 2MnO(OH)(s) + Zn(OH)_2(s)$

89. The electrolysis cell for electroplating copper:

anode: $Cu(s) \rightarrow Cu^{+2}(aq) + 2e^-$

cathode: $Cu^{+2}(aq) + 2e^- \rightarrow Cu(s)$

Corrosion

91. a) yes
    b) no
    c) yes

Cumulative Problems

93. a) Redox reaction with Zn being oxidized and Co being reduced.
    b) Not a redox reaction.
    c) Not a redox reaction.
    d) Redox reaction with K being oxidized and Br_2 being reduced.

95. 1: $\underset{+7}{MnO_4^-}(aq) + \underset{0}{Zn}(s) \rightarrow \underset{+2}{Mn^{+2}}(aq) + \underset{+2}{Zn^{+2}}(aq)$

2: $MnO_4^- \rightarrow Mn^{+2}$ $\qquad\qquad\qquad$ $Zn \rightarrow Zn^{+2}$

3: $MnO_4^- + 8H^+ \rightarrow Mn^{+2} + 4H_2O$ $\qquad$ $Zn \rightarrow Zn^{+2}$

4: $MnO_4^- + 8H^+ + 5e^- \rightarrow Mn^{+2} + 4H_2O$ $\qquad$ $Zn \rightarrow Zn^{+2} + 2e^-$

5: $2MnO_4^- + 16H^+ + 10e^- \rightarrow 2Mn^{+2} + 8H_2O$ $\qquad$ $5Zn \rightarrow 5Zn^{+2} + 10e^-$

6: $2MnO_4^-(aq) + 16H^+(aq) + 5Zn(s) \rightarrow 2Mn^{+2}(aq) + 8H_2O(l) + 5Zn^{+2}(aq)$

$$2.85 \text{ g Zn} \times \frac{1 \text{ mol Zn}}{65.39 \text{ g}} \times \frac{2 \text{ mol KMnO}_4}{5 \text{ mol Zn}} \times \frac{1 \text{ L}}{0.500 \text{ mol KMnO}_4} = 0.0349 \text{ L}$$

97. $5.8 \text{ g Ag} \times \dfrac{1 \text{ mol Ag}}{107.9 \text{ g}} \times \dfrac{1 \text{ mol e}^-}{1 \text{ mol Ag}} = 0.054 \text{ mol e}^-$

99. a) $6HI + 2Cr \rightarrow 2Cr^{+3} + 3H_2 + 6I^-$

$5.95 \text{ g Cr} \times \dfrac{1 \text{ mol Cr}}{52.00 \text{ g}} \times \dfrac{6 \text{ mol HI}}{2 \text{ mol Cr}} \times \dfrac{1 \text{ L}}{3.5 \text{ mol HI}} = 0.098 \text{ L}$

b) $6HI + 2Al \rightarrow 2Al^{+3} + 3H_2 + 6I^-$

$2.15 \text{ g Al} \times \dfrac{1 \text{ mol Al}}{26.98 \text{ g}} \times \dfrac{6 \text{ mol HI}}{2 \text{ mol Al}} \times \dfrac{1 \text{ L}}{3.5 \text{ mol HI}} = 0.068 \text{ L}$

c) no reaction

d) no reaction

Highlight Problems

101. The sketch should show aluminum atoms going into solution as +3 ions, which dissolve the metal electrode. The copper ions are forming solid, elemental copper atoms on the aluminum strip.

103. The sketch should show fewer zinc atoms making up the solid anode and more Zn^{+2} ions in solution. Also, there should be fewer Ni^{+2} ions in solution and more Ni atoms on the cathode.

Radioactivity and Nuclear Chemistry

17

Questions

1. Radioactivity is the emission of tiny, invisible (to the human eye) particles by the nuclei of certain atoms. A radioactive atom will spontaneously emit these tiny, invisible particles.

3. Becquerel first discovered radioactivity in 1896 by placing radioactive uranium minerals on photographic plates in an attempt to look for X-rays.

5. Marie Sklodowska Curie discovered two new elements that were both radioactive, which is a term that she created to replace the term uranic rays.

7. A = mass number, Z = atomic number, and X = chemical symbol

9. Alpha (α) radiation occurs when the nucleus emits a particle that contains 2 protons and 2 neutrons. Alpha particles are symbolized by $_2^4\text{He}$.

11. Alpha particles have a high ionizing power in comparison with other radioactive particles, however it has very low penetrating power in comparison with the other radioactive particles.

13. When an atom emits a beta particle it gains a proton, becoming an atom of the next heavier element.

15. Gamma radiation is a type of electromagnetic radiation that is essentially a high energy photon. The gamma particle is symbolized by $_0^0\gamma$.

17. Gamma rays have low ionizing power and high penetrating power in comparison with other radioactive particles.

19. When an atom emits a positron, it converts a proton to a neutron, which makes it into an atom of the next heavier element.

21. A nuclear equation represents nuclear processes such as radioactivity. For a nuclear equation to be balanced, the sum of the atomic numbers on both sides of the equation must be equal, and the sum of the mass numbers on both sides of the equation must be equal.

23. A film-badge dosimeter is a radioactivity detector used as a safety precaution for people who work with or near radioactive compounds. The dosimeter is a small piece of photographic film that is attached to clothing and regularly collected and developed in order to monitor the amount of radioactivity to which the badge has been exposed to in the recent past.

25. In a scintillation counter, the radioactive particles pass through a crystal of NaI or CsI, which emits UV-Vis photons as it becomes excited by the radioactive particles. The photons are then converted into an electrical signal.

27. The half-life of a radioactive nuclide is the time it will take for ½ of the original parent nuclides to undergo decay.

29. Radon in the environment comes from the radioactive decay series of uranium. It presents a danger because radon is a gaseous compound and its daughter nuclides can attach to dust particles, which can be inhaled into the human body.

31. Carbon-14 is converted into carbon dioxide and then into plant material during photosynthesis. Since animals ingest plant material, all living organisms contain a residual amount of carbon-14 . The carbon-14 level is continuous, as all living organisms continually ingest new amounts of carbon-14.

33. Carbon-14 has been proven accurate by measuring the levels of carbon-14 in objects that are of <u>known</u> age, proving it is an accurate method. For example, tree rings from trees that are hundreds of years old can be used to test accuracy. Carbon-14 dating is limited to about 50,000 year old objects because the amount of radioactive carbon is too small to accurately measure in older objects.

35. Nuclear fission is the process of splitting a nucleus into smaller elements. The first fission experiment was conducted by Enrico Fermi, although he did not realize that his reaction had undergone the fission process. Meitner, Strassmann, and Hahn were the first to report that bombarding uranium-235 with neutrons produces a fission reaction.

37. A critical mass is the minimum amount of uranium needed to create a chain reaction.

39. The heat generated by a controlled nuclear fission reaction is used to boil water and the steam produced turns turbines, which generate the electricity.

41. The main benefits of nuclear electricity generation are that it requires very little fuel and does not generate air pollution or greenhouse gases.

43. A nuclear power plant cannot detonate like a nuclear bomb because the uranium fuel is not enriched with the quantity of uranium-235 that is needed to produce a bomb.

45. The traditional nuclear bombs are of the fission type. However, hydrogen bombs are based on a fusion reaction. It should be noted that in order for a hydrogen bomb to work, a small fission reaction takes place to generate sufficient heat to initiate the fusion reaction.

47. Radiation can ionize molecules in living organisms.

49. Radiation can increase the risk of cancer because it can damage DNA, which can cause cells to grow abnormally.

51. The main unit of radiation is the roentgen equivalent man, aka rem. A typical person is exposed to one-third of a rem per year.

53. Isotope scanning is a method used to diagnose different diseases based on the use of radioactive isotopes and their ability to target different organs and tissues. The radioactive isotopes are detected with either photographic film or a scintillation counter.

Isotopic and Nuclear Particle Symbols

55. $^{207}_{82}\text{Pb}$

57. Protons (Z): 81
    Neutrons (A−Z): 126

59. a) beta particle
    b) neutron
    c) gamma ray

61. a) $^{234}_{92}U \rightarrow \ ^{230}_{90}Th + \ ^{4}_{2}He$

    b) $^{230}_{90}Th \rightarrow \ ^{226}_{88}Ra + \ ^{4}_{2}He$

    c) $^{226}_{88}Ra \rightarrow \ ^{222}_{86}Rn + \ ^{4}_{2}He$

    d) $^{222}_{86}Rn \rightarrow \ ^{218}_{84}Po + \ ^{4}_{2}He$

63. a) $^{214}_{82}Pb \rightarrow \ ^{214}_{83}Bi + \ ^{0}_{-1}e$

    b) $^{214}_{83}Bi \rightarrow \ ^{214}_{84}Po + \ ^{0}_{-1}e$

    c) $^{231}_{90}Th \rightarrow \ ^{231}_{91}Pa + \ ^{0}_{-1}e$

    d) $^{227}_{89}Ac \rightarrow \ ^{227}_{90}Th + \ ^{0}_{-1}e$

65. a) $^{11}_{6}C \rightarrow \ ^{11}_{5}B + \ ^{0}_{+1}e$

    b) $^{13}_{7}N \rightarrow \ ^{13}_{6}C + \ ^{0}_{+1}e$

    c) $^{15}_{8}O \rightarrow \ ^{15}_{7}N + \ ^{0}_{+1}e$

67. $^{241}_{94}Pu \rightarrow \ ^{241}_{95}Am + \underline{\ ^{0}_{-1}e}$

    $^{241}_{95}Am \rightarrow \ ^{237}_{93}Np + \underline{\ ^{4}_{2}He}$

    $^{237}_{93}Np \rightarrow \underline{\ ^{233}_{91}Pa} + \ ^{4}_{2}He$

    $\underline{^{233}_{91}Pa} \rightarrow \ ^{233}_{92}U + \ ^{0}_{-1}e$

69. $^{232}_{90}Th \rightarrow \ ^{228}_{88}Ra + \ ^{4}_{2}He$

    $^{228}_{88}Ra \rightarrow \ ^{228}_{89}Ac + \ ^{0}_{-1}e$

    $^{228}_{89}Ac \rightarrow \ ^{228}_{90}Th + \ ^{0}_{-1}e$

    $^{228}_{90}Th \rightarrow \ ^{224}_{88}Ra + \ ^{4}_{2}He$

Half-Life

71. $1000 \xrightarrow{\text{2 days}} 500 \xrightarrow{\text{2 days}} 250 \xrightarrow{\text{2 days}} 125 \xrightarrow{\text{2 days}} 62.5 \xrightarrow{\text{2 days}} 31.25$
Approximately 31 atoms remain.

73. $5.0 \times 10^{-2} \xrightarrow{\text{6 hrs}} 2.5 \times 10^{-2} \xrightarrow{\text{6 hrs}} 1.25 \times 10^{-2} \xrightarrow{\text{6 hrs}} 6.25 \times 10^{-3}$
It would take 18 hrs for technetium-99 to decay to 6.3×10^{-3} mg.

75. $2.80 \xrightarrow{\text{1st}} 1.40 \xrightarrow{\text{2nd}} 0.70 \xrightarrow{\text{3rd}} 0.35 \xrightarrow{\text{4th}} 0.175 \xrightarrow{\text{5th}} 0.0875$
It would take 5 half lives or 1.2×10^6 years.

77. $1.55 \xrightarrow{\text{3.8 days}} 0.775 \xrightarrow{\text{3.8 days}} 0.388 \xrightarrow{\text{3.8 days}} 0.194$
There would be 0.194 grams of the isotope after 11.4 days.

79. Ga-67 > P-32 > Cr-51 > Sr-89

Radiocarbon Dating

81. The age of the boat would be equal to one half-life of C-14, or approximately 5,730 years old.

83. The skull has undergone six half-lives of C-14, which would make it approximately 34,380 years old.

Fission and Fusion

85. $^{235}_{92}\text{U} + ^{1}_{0}\text{n} \rightarrow ^{144}_{54}\text{Xe} + ^{90}_{38}\text{Sr} + ^{1}_{0}\text{n}$,   One neutron is produced.

87. $^{2}_{1}\text{H} + ^{2}_{1}\text{H} \rightarrow ^{3}_{2}\text{He} + ^{1}_{0}\text{n}$

Cumulative Problems

89. $\dfrac{3.2 \times 10^{-11} \text{ J}}{\text{atom}} \times \dfrac{6.022 \times 10^{23} \text{ atoms}}{1 \text{ mol U}} = 1.9 \times 10^{13} \text{ J/mol}$

$\dfrac{1.9 \times 10^{13} \text{ J}}{\text{mol}} \times \dfrac{1 \text{ mol U}}{238.03 \text{ g}} \times \dfrac{1000 \text{ g}}{1 \text{ kg}} = 8.1 \times 10^{13} \text{ J/kg}$

91. In one half-life (5 days), we will lose 0.60 g of material. Assuming that each atom produces one beta particle in the decay process, the number of beta emissions is

$$0.60 \text{ g Bi} \times \frac{1 \text{ mol Bi}}{208.98 \text{ g}} \times \frac{6.022 \times 10^{23} \text{ atoms}}{1 \text{ mol Bi}} \times \frac{1 \text{ } \beta \text{ particle}}{1 \text{ atom}} = 1.7 \times 10^{21} \beta \text{ particles}$$

93. $\dfrac{0.400 \text{ rem}}{0.585 \text{ rem}} \times 100\% = 68.4\%$ due to radon

Highlight Problems

95. The missing nucleus contains 9 protons and 7 neutrons (Fluorine-16).

97. The missing nucleus contains 6 protons and 4 neutrons (Carbon-10).

Organic Chemistry

18

Questions

1. Organic molecules are responsible for most odors.

3. At the end of the 18th century, organic molecules were considered those molecules that came from living sources. Inorganic compounds were considered those molecules that came from the earth.

5. Vitalism was proven incorrect in 1828 by Friedrich Wöhler when he was able to successfully synthesis urea, a compound previously only isolated from urine.

7. a) tetrahedral
    b) trigonal planar
    c) linear

9. The main uses of hydrocarbons are as fuels and as raw materials in the synthesis of many products, including fabrics, soaps, dyes, cosmetics, drugs, plastic, and rubber.

11. Alkanes are considered saturated hydrocarbons because they contain only single bonds and they have the maximum number of hydrogen atoms possible (i.e., saturated). Alkenes and alkynes are considered unsaturated hydrocarbons because they contain double and triple bonds, and therefore have fewer hydrogen atoms than the similar alkane compound.

13. The n-alkane compounds have all carbon atoms bonded in a straight chain, where the branched alkanes have branches of carbon atoms coming off of a main straight chain of carbon atoms.

15. Alkenes are hydrocarbons that contain at least one double bond between carbon atoms, where alkanes only contain single bonds.

17. Hydrocarbon combustion reactions are the burning of hydrocarbons in the presence of oxygen. An example of a hydrocarbon combustion reaction is:

$$CH_3CH_2CH_3(g) + 5O_2(g) \rightarrow 3CO_2(g) + 4H_2O(g)$$

19. Alkene addition reactions occur when atoms add across the double bond. An example of an alkene addition reaction is:

$$CH_2 = CH_2(g) + Cl_2(g) \rightarrow CH_2ClCH_2Cl(g)$$

21. Two common ways of showing the structure of benzene are:

23. The generic structure of alcohols is ROH. Two examples of alcohols are ethanol: CH_3CH_2OH and 1-butanol: $CH_3CH_2CH_2CH_2OH$.

25. The generic structure of ethers is R-O-R. Two examples ethers are dimethyl ether: CH_3OCH_3 and diethyl ether: $CH_3CH_2OCH_2CH_3$.

27. The generic structure of aldehydes is $R-\overset{\displaystyle O}{\overset{\|}{C}}-H$, and the generic structure of ketones is $R-\overset{\displaystyle O}{\overset{\|}{C}}-R$. The structure of acetaldehyde is $CH_3-\overset{\displaystyle O}{\overset{\|}{C}}-H$, and the structure of acetone is $CH_3-\overset{\displaystyle O}{\overset{\|}{C}}-CH_3$.

29. The generic structure of carboxylic acid is $R-\overset{\displaystyle O}{\overset{\|}{C}}-OH$, and the generic structure of esters is $R-\overset{\displaystyle O}{\overset{\|}{C}}-OR$. The structure of acetic acid is $CH_3-\overset{\displaystyle O}{\overset{\|}{C}}-OH$, and the structure of propanoic acid is $CH_3-CH_2-\overset{\displaystyle O}{\overset{\|}{C}}-OH$.

31. The generic structure of amines is NR_3. Examples of specific amines is ammonia $H-\overset{\displaystyle H}{\overset{|}{N}}-H$ and ethylamine $CH_3CH_2-\overset{\displaystyle H}{\overset{|}{N}}-H$.

33. A polymer is a long, chainlike molecule that is made up of small repeating units called monomers. A polymer is made up of one type of monomer, where a copolymer has two different monomers.

Hydrocarbons

35. Choices c and d are hydrocarbons because they contain only C and H.

37. a) alkane
    b) alkene
    c) alkyne
    d) alkene

Alkanes

39. a)
$$H-\underset{\underset{H}{|}}{\overset{\overset{H}{|}}{C}}-\underset{\underset{H}{|}}{\overset{\overset{H}{|}}{C}}-H \Rightarrow CH_3CH_3$$

b)
$$H-\underset{\underset{H}{|}}{\overset{\overset{H}{|}}{C}}-\underset{\underset{H}{|}}{\overset{\overset{H}{|}}{C}}-\underset{\underset{H}{|}}{\overset{\overset{H}{|}}{C}}-\underset{\underset{H}{|}}{\overset{\overset{H}{|}}{C}}-H \Rightarrow CH_3CH_2CH_2CH_3$$

c)
$$H-\underset{\underset{H}{|}}{\overset{\overset{H}{|}}{C}}-\underset{\underset{H}{|}}{\overset{\overset{H}{|}}{C}}-\underset{\underset{H}{|}}{\overset{\overset{H}{|}}{C}}-\underset{\underset{H}{|}}{\overset{\overset{H}{|}}{C}}-\underset{\underset{H}{|}}{\overset{\overset{H}{|}}{C}}-H \Rightarrow CH_3CH_2CH_2CH_2CH_3$$

d)
$$H-\underset{\underset{H}{|}}{\overset{\overset{H}{|}}{C}}-H \Rightarrow CH_4$$

41. Two isomers of butane:

$$H_3C-\underset{\overset{|}{CH_3}}{CH}-CH_3 \qquad H_3C-CH_2-CH_2-CH_3$$

43. Five isomers of hexane:

45.
a) n-pentane
b) 2-methylbutane
c) 4-ethyl-2-methylhexane
d) 3,3-dimethylpentane

47. Alkane structures:

49.
a) n-pentane
b) 3-methylhexane
c) 2,3-dimethylpentane

51. $\overset{\text{H}}{\underset{}{\text{H}-\text{C}}}=\overset{\text{H}}{\underset{}{\text{C}}}-\text{H} \Rightarrow \text{CH}_2\text{CH}_2$

$\overset{\text{H}}{\underset{}{\text{H}-\text{C}}}=\overset{\text{H}}{\underset{}{\text{C}}}-\overset{\text{H}}{\underset{\text{H}}{\text{C}}}-\text{H} \Rightarrow \text{CH}_2\text{CHCH}_3$

53. $\overset{\text{H}}{\underset{\text{H}}{\text{H}-\text{C}}}=\overset{\text{H}}{\underset{\text{H}}{\text{C}}}-\overset{\text{H}}{\underset{\text{H}}{\text{C}}}-\overset{\text{H}}{\underset{\text{H}}{\text{C}}}-\overset{\text{H}}{\underset{\text{H}}{\text{C}}}-\text{H}$ $\overset{\text{H}}{\underset{\text{H}}{\text{H}-\text{C}}}-\overset{\text{H}}{\underset{\text{H}}{\text{C}}}=\overset{\text{H}}{\underset{\text{H}}{\text{C}}}-\overset{\text{H}}{\underset{\text{H}}{\text{C}}}-\overset{\text{H}}{\underset{\text{H}}{\text{C}}}-\text{H}$

55. a) 2-pentene
    b) 4-methyl-2-pentene
    c) 3,3-dimethyl-1-butene
    d) 3,4-dimethyl-1-hexene

57. a) 2-butyne
    b) 4-methyl-2-pentyne
    c) 4,4-dimethyl-2-hexyne
    d) 3-ethyl-3-methyl-1-pentyne

59. The structures:

61. The isomers are:

a) H_3C—CH_2—$C\equiv C$—CH_2—CH_2—CH_2—CH_3

b) CH_2=CH—CH_2—CH_2—CH_3

c) $HC\equiv C$—$\overset{\displaystyle CH_3}{\underset{\displaystyle CH_3}{C}}$—$CH_2$—$CH_3$

d) H_3C—CH=$\overset{\displaystyle CH_3}{C}$—$\overset{\displaystyle CH_2-CH_3}{CH}$—$CH_2$—$CH_2$—$CH_2$—$CH_3$

Hydrocarbon Reactions

63. a) $2CH_3CH_3(g) + 7O_2(g) \rightarrow 4CO_2(g) + 6H_2O(g)$

    b) $2CH_2$=$CHCH_3(g) + 9O_2(g) \rightarrow 6CO_2(g) + 6H_2O(g)$

    c) $2CH\equiv CH(g) + 5O_2(g) \rightarrow 4CO_2(g) + 2H_2O(g)$

65. $CH_4(g) + Br_2(g) \rightarrow CH_3Br(g) + HBr(g)$

67. CH_3CH=$CHCH_3(g) + Cl_2(g) \rightarrow CH_3CHClCHClCH_3(g)$

69. CH_2=$CH_2(g) + H_2(g) \rightarrow CH_3CH_3(g)$

Aromatic Hydrocarbons

71. The structural formula that represents both shorthand formulas is:

73. a) fluorobenzene
    b) isopropylbenzene
    c) ethylbenzene

144

75. a) 4-phenyloctane
    b) 5-phenyl-3-heptene
    c) 7-phenyl-2-heptyne

77. a) 1-bromo-2-chlorobenzene
    b) 1,2-diethylbenzene or orthodiethylbenzene or o-diethylbenzene
    c) 1,3-difluorobenzene or metadichlorobenzene or m-dichlorobenzene

79. The structures:

Functional Groups

83. a) amine

$H_3C-CH_2-CH_2-NH$ with CH_3 (circled CH_2-NH / CH_3)

b) aldehyde

$H_3C-CH_2-CH_2-CH$ with $=O$ (circled CH with O)

c) alcohol

$H_3C-C(CH_3)(CH_3)-C(CH_3)(CH_3)-OH$ (circled $C-OH$)

d) ether

$H_3C-C(CH_3)(CH_3)-O-CH_2-CH_3$ (circled $C-O-CH_2$)

Alcohols

85. a) 2-butanol
     b) 2-methyl-1-propanol
     c) 3-ethyl-1-hexanol
     d) 3-methyl-3-pentanol

Ethers

87. a) diethyl ether
     b) ethyl propyl ether
     c) dipropyl ether
     d) pentyl propyl ether

Aldehydes and Ketones

89. a) butanal
     b) 2-pentanone
     c) 4-heptanone
     d) heptanal

Carboxylic Acids and Esters

91. a) butanoic acid
    b) methyl ethanoate
    c) propyl propanoate
    d) heptanoic acid

Amines

93. a) triethylamine
    b) butylpropylamine
    c) isopropylamine

Polymers

95. The structure of polyisobutylene is:

97. The dimer structure:

Cumulative Problems

99. a) alcohol
    b) amine
    c) alkane
    d) carboxylic acid
    e) ether
    f) alkene

101. a) 3-methyl-4-tert-butylheptane
     b) 3-methyl butanal
     c) 4-isopropyl-3-methyl-2-heptene
     d) propyl butanoate

103. a) same molecule
     b) isomers
     c) same molecule

105. $CH_3CH=CHCH_3 + H_2 \rightarrow CH_3CH_2CH_2CH_3$

$$15.5 \text{ kg 2-butene} \times \frac{1 x 10^3 \text{ g}}{1 \text{ kg}} \times \frac{1 \text{ mol 2-butene}}{56.10 \text{ g}} \times \frac{1 \text{ mol } H_2}{1 \text{ mol 2-butene}} \times \frac{2.016 \text{ g}}{1 \text{ mol } H_2}$$

$$= 557 \text{ g } H_2$$

Highlights

107. a) alcohol
     b) amine
     c) carboxylic acid
     d) ester
     e) alkane
     f) ether

Biochemistry

19

Questions

1. The goal of the Human Genome Project was to map all of the genetic material (genome) of a human being.

3. The benefits of the Human Genome Project are expected to include the ability to identify persons who are genetically predisposed to contracting certain diseases and the ability to design new drugs to fight diseases.

5. Carbohydrates are molecules that are the main source for short-term energy storage in living organisms.

7. Glucose is soluble in water because of the many OH groups that allow water to hydrogen bond to glucose. This is important because glucose needs to be transported by blood to the cells and then through the cell wall into the aqueous interior of the cell.

9. During digestion, disaccharides and polysaccharides are broken down into the simpler monosaccharide units.

11. Starch and cellulose are both polysaccharides but the difference is the bond angles that form between saccharide units. Because of the difference in bond angle, humans can digest starch and use it for energy, while cellulose cannot be digested and passes directly through humans.

13. The main functions of lipids are as structural units of cells, long-term energy storage, and insulation.

15. The general structure of a fatty acid is $R-\overset{\overset{\displaystyle O}{\displaystyle \|}}{C}-OH$ where R is from 3 to 19 carbon atoms long.

17. Triglycerides are tri-esters composed of glycerol and three fatty acids. Oils and fats are triglycerides.

19. A saturated fat is made up of saturated fatty acids and is a solid at room temperature. An unsaturated fat is made up of unsaturated fatty acids and is a liquid at room temperature.

21. The main function of phospholipids and glycolipids in the body is as components of cell walls.

23. Steroids serve as male and female hormones in the body.

25. Proteins have many roles in the body such as catalysts, structural unit of muscle, skin and cartilage, transportation of oxygen, disease fighting antibodies, and as hormones.

27. Amino acids differ from each other by the nature of the R group.

29. The formation of a peptide bond:

31. The primary protein structure simply refers to the sequence of amino acids in the protein chain. The primary protein structure is maintained by the peptide bonds formed between the amino acids.

33. The tertiary protein structure refers to the large scale bends and folds in the protein structure. The tertiary protein structure results from interactions between individual amino acid R units that are separated from each other by a large distance along the linear sequence of amino acids.

35. The α-helix structure occurs when the amino acid chain is wrapped into a tight coil, much the same as a spring, with the R groups extending outward. The β-pleated sheet structure has an extended chain that is in a zigzag pattern.

37. Nucleic acids are a chemical code that specifies the correct amino acid sequences for the creation of proteins.

39. The four bases found within DNA are: adenine (A), cytosine (C), guanine (G), and thymine (T).

41. The genetic code links a specific codon to an amino acid.

43. A gene is a sequence of codons within a DNA molecule that provides the code for a specific protein.

45. A chromosome is the structure that contains the genes.

47. No, cells only produce those proteins that are critical to the cell type and function.

49. a) thymine (T)
    b) adenine (A)
    c) guanine (G)
    d) cytosine (C)

Problems

Carbohydrates

51. a) carbohydrate, monosaccharide
    b) not a carbohydrate
    c) not a carbohydrate
    d) carbohydrate, disaccharide

53. a) hexose
    b) tetrose
    c) pentose
    d) tetrose

55. The linear and ring structures for glucose are:

57. The structure of sucrose:

 Glucose   Fructose

151

59. a) lipid-fatty acid-saturated
    b) lipid-steroid
    c) lipid-triglyceride-unsaturated
    d) not a lipid

61. The block diagram of a triglyceride is:

63. The structure of the triglyceride is shown below and because it is an unsaturated fat, you would expect it to be a liquid.

Amino Acids and Proteins

65. a) not an amino acid
    b) amino acid
    c) not an amino acid
    d) amino acid

67. The reaction between valine and leucine is:

69. The tripeptide structures are:

71. This interaction is an example of a tertiary structure because the amino acids involved are a long distance apart in terms of their placement in the chain.

73. A listing of the amino acids in order of their appearance in the chain is a primary structure.

Nucleic Acids

75. a) nucleotide, G
    b) not a nucleotide
    c) not a nucleotide
    d) not a nucleotide

77. The complementary strand of DNA is: T T A C G C G

79. DNA replicates as follows:

1. Hydrogen bonds break   2. Complementary bases   3. Hydrogen bonds reform
                                        match to each strand

Cumulative Problems

81. a) glycoside linkage—carbohydrates
    b) peptide bonds—proteins
    c) ester linkage—triglycerides

83. a) glucose—short-term energy storage
    b) DNA—blueprint for proteins
    c) phopholipids—compose cell membranes
    d) triglycerides—long-term energy storage.

85. a) codon—codes for a single amino acid
    b) gene—codes for a single protein
    c) genome—all of the genetic material of an organism
    d) chromosome—structure that contains genes